Volume 7
EARTHMOVING MACHINERY
FIBRE

The ILLUSTRATED
SCIENCE *and*
INVENTION
ENCYCLOPEDIA

International Edition

H.S. STUTTMAN CO., INC. *publishers*   New York, N.Y. 10016

how it works

Published by H. S. STUTTMAN CO., Inc.
New York, N.Y. 10016
© Marshall Cavendish Limited 1974, 1976, 1977

EARTHMOVING MACHINERY

Great advances have been made in the last three decades in the design of the earthmoving machinery used in construction and public works engineering. Even with the latest machinery, however, the basic method of earthmoving remains as it has always been: the ground is broken up, loaded into some form of transport, and carried away. There may be a separate machine for each function, but more usually the machines used are capable of more than one task.

Excavators There are several types of excavator in use today which can cope with any kind of material from mud to broken rock, but all work most effectively when the spoil consistency allows the digging bucket to be completely filled at each working cycle. Hydraulic excavators are steadily replacing the older cable (wire rope) operated kind, except for *dragline* work. A dragline excavator is a CRANE-like machine, usually running on crawler tracks, with a digging bucket hung from the jib on a cable. The dragline itself is attached to the

bucket and wound round a winch at the base of the jib. In operation, the bucket is swung forward on to the ground, and fills as it is dragged back along the ground by the dragline. Draglining is particularly effective in removing underwater spoil, and in working with sand and ballast. In DEMOLITION work, dragline excavators are widely used both for clearing rubble and, with a steel ball in place of the bucket, for the demolition itself. Dragline excavators can also be used with 'clamshell' buckets or grabs to clean out restricted corners, and may in addition be used as cranes for handling and placing materials and components. (See also EXCAVATOR, HYDRAULIC.)

Bucket-wheel excavators are designed to cut away material from the sides of a bank or slope by the cutting edges of a

Below : a close-up of the cutting wheel of a large bucket-wheel type excavator used for scooping up crushed ore at a works in Western Australia. Machines like this are in use all over the world for moving loose materials such as ores and coal, as well as for excavation work.

COLORIFIC

number of buckets mounted radially around the rim of a large wheel. This wheel, rotated under power, is carried at the end of a large boom that can be raised, lowered and swung so that a continuous cutting action can be maintained. Spoil is deposited by the buckets as they invert on to a system of belt CONVEYERS that carry it away to either a tip or to some form of transport.

Most bucket-wheel excavators are huge—some are among the largest of self-propelled land machines—and they are well established in such applications as opencast COAL MINING where, for all practical purposes, the quantities of material to be moved at a particular site can be considered limitless. At the other end of the scale, work is going on to develop much smaller machines which would be suitable for ordinary public works projects. Some extremely large dragline excavators are also in use in opencast mines and quarries.

Loaders

Crawler-mounted loaders, commonly confused with the outwardly similar BULLDOZERS although their functions are usually quite different, are among the most generally useful earthmoving machines. The crawler loader is particularly suited to work on demolition and rough site clearance, where its ability to manoeuvre in confined surroundings outweighs

Below: the largest dragline excavator in Europe, at an opencast coal mine near Morpeth in Northumberland, England. Known as 'Big Geordie', it weighs 3,000 tons; the bucket can hold about 100 tons of earth, and is carried on a boom 265 ft (81 m) long.

its disadvantage of a limited top speed. The main difference between crawler loaders and bulldozers is that they have a large loading bucket at the front instead of a blade, but they both have the advantage of being able to work on broken rock, concrete, or other jagged debris which would quickly ruin pneumatic tyres.

Wheeled loaders are used where ground conditions are good and the bucket can be filled without tyre-destroying wheelspin. They are usually fast and capable of making rapid turns, and can run as quickly in reverse as in the forward direction. They are often found in materials handling applications, and the largest and most robust models are able to provide satisfactory performance in quite arduous quarrying and similar applications, due mainly to improvements in tyre design.

Scrapers

The development of large, reliable tyres has aided the development of motor scrapers, machines which are used wherever ground conditions are suitable, for moving quantities of soil over moderate distances. Essentially the motor scraper is a big open-fronted box, mounted on wheels and driven by a large DIESEL ENGINE, and whose leading edge can be pushed a little way into the ground. As the vehicle moves forward the box fills, the load being pushed out at the discharge point by a moving bulkhead, which gives a controlled discharge as the machine continues to move forward.

Tyre life is a dominant factor in the economics of motor scraper operation, and a recent development seeks to lessen the

resistance to loading by breaking up the layer of material with a series of beater bars arranged to rotate just above the cutting edge of the box.

Adverse conditions, notably sharp stones in the earth or soil too soft to carry the high point loadings of a motor scraper, have also led to the continued use of the original type of scraper, the scraper trailer. This is just a large scraper box mounted on wheels and pulled along by a crawler TRACTOR. Scraper trailers and motor scrapers are widely used in highway construction and similar applications.

Dumpers Very few kinds of earthmoving machinery are adapted to moving material more than a few paces, and most depend on some kind of vehicle to move the spoil from one place to another. Quite often standard roadgoing trucks are used, particularly when public highways have to be traversed, although a common modification made to improve traction on poor ground is to transmit the drive to all of the wheels. Such vehicles are, however, not sufficiently robust to withstand the conditions encountered in earthmoving applications and, since reliability is usually more important than first cost, most transport is specially built and very sturdy. The tipping mechanism is usually powered either by screw jacks driven by the vehicle engine, or by hydraulic rams.

Vehicle sizes range from about 20 tons payload up to 200 tons, although 100 tons is accepted as being the maximum capacity currently practicable on two axles, while the economics

WILLIAM MACQUITTY

Above: a large bulldozer fitted with a 'ripper' attachment, which is used rather like a plough to break up hard ground. When the ground has been broken up with the ripper the loosened material can be moved with the bulldozing blade in the normal way.

Below: a purpose-built heavy duty dump truck, with four wheels per axle. A wheeled loader can be seen in the background.

INTERNATIONAL HARVESTER

of bulk earthmoving tend to favour 50-ton vehicles as the dumper capacity and size must be matched to the excavating and loading equipment.

At the other end of the scale there is a wide range of small dump trucks in use on construction and demolition sites, working as replacements for hand barrows and carts. The skip is at the front, and hinged so that it can tip forward to discharge its load when the securing latch is released. The skip is designed so that the weight of the load acts in front of the pivots, so that when the latch is released the skip will tip with little or no assistance. Small dumpers are usually powered by a small air-cooled diesel engine, which drives the front wheels, and the steering acts on the rear wheels.

Continuous working The bucket-wheel excavator and the belt conveyor have the advantage of operating continuously, unlike other machines which spend only a fraction of their time actually digging and carrying. The search for other means of continuous working has, in a limited way, been very successful, and an established way of excavating and moving sand, ballast, clay and other materials is to wash it free with jets of water and then pump the resulting slurry through large pipelines. This is similar to the methods used in the extraction of CHINA CLAY, and huge quantities can be moved over considerable distances in this way. A great deal of land reclamation is carried out in this way, while essentially similar techniques are used by

suction DREDGERS to deepen waterways.

Attempts to replace conventional hard ground digging machinery with other methods have so far been largely unsuccessful. The use of controlled nuclear explosions to produce major excavations has been suggested but is as yet untried, although great quantities of conventional explosives are in daily use. Ultrasonics (high frequency sound vibrations) are a possible means of breaking up ground and rocks, but an effective way of using this technique has not yet been found.

Proposals to use air-cushion type carriers in place of wheeled or tracked vehicles have so far found little response, as the advantages of dispensing with expensive gears, tyres, tracks and transmissions are outweighed by the need to keep machines as versatile as possible.

ECHO SOUNDING (see asdic & sonar)

Below left: a typical small dumper truck of the type widely used on building and demolition sites. The engine is mounted at the rear next to the driver, and drives the front wheels only, the rear wheels being used for steering. In the picture the driver has just pulled the lever that releases the skip, which is beginning to tip forward to dump its load. This model has a skip capacity of 1.5 tons.

Below right: a large motor scraper. A similar looking machine, the grader, has a bulldozer-type blade in place of the scraper box.

WINGET

EDDY CURRENTS

As the term suggests, eddy currents are a phenomenon of things that flow, and this includes fluids such as water and air or less tangible things such as an electric current. When liquid flows, such as water flowing from a tap, it may do so in an orderly manner, almost as if it were still flowing in a pipe. But if the tap lacks the right shape of nozzle, the water falls out of it in an irregular manner, with droplets separating from the main stream, whose general shape is constantly changing. Such flow is called *turbulent*. Smooth flow is called *laminar* because the fluid need not flow at the same rate throughout the cross-section of the stream, but can flow in thin layers (*laminae*) which can slide over each other smoothly.

The same two kinds of flow can refer to the passage of air over the wings of an aircraft, laminar flow being desirable and turbulent flow occurring under certain circumstances, for example when the aircraft stalls. High-speed motor boats and cars are streamlined in an attempt to create laminar flow, but even a streamlined motor boat leaves little whirlpools behind it in the water. It was these whirlpools which were first given the name 'eddy currents' or 'eddies'.

In modern technology the term is given different interpretations by different authors. Some would imply that an eddy current contains a rotating component, while others use the expression to denote irregular or turbulent flow in general.

The term is often used to describe electric currents flowing in a large sheet of conducting metal, as opposed to current flowing in an ordered manner in a wire, where insulating material is used to prevent the current from taking short cuts from one turn of a coil to the next.

In electrical terminology, eddy currents are almost entirely associated with electromagnetic induction, that strange phenomenon whereby a moving or changing magnetic field passing through a conducting material induces a current in it. Thus a magnet pulled across a sheet of copper, aluminium or brass will produce irregular current flow, including whirlpools very similar to those found in the wake of a ship. The phenomenon is used in household electricity METERS and in electromagnetic clutches. The current always tries to effectively oppose the relative motion between sheet and magnet. To put it another way, the magnet effectively tries to drag the sheet along with it.

The use of the phrase 'eddy current' is extended by some authors to the rotating part of an induction motor (see ELECTRIC MOTOR) on the grounds that the rotor consists not of insulated wires but of a copper or aluminium 'cage', the bars of which are sunk in slots in an iron core. The definition usually assumed is, however, that an eddy current infers a randomness which is not to be found in an induction motor, for the designers of such machines go to considerable trouble to ensure that the induced currents are highly organized.

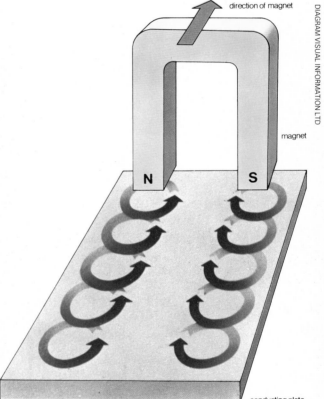

direction of magnet

magnet

N S

conducting plate

Above: when a permanent magnet is moved across the surface of a metal — for example, aluminium — turbulent electrical currents called 'eddy currents' are produced in the metal. Although these currents are random in nature they produce their own magnetic fields which create a dragging force between the plate and the magnet.

INTERNATIONAL HARVESTER

DIAGRAM VISUAL INFORMATION LTD

EDISON, Thomas Alva (1847-1931)

Thomas Alva Edison was the most famous and prolific inventor of all time. During his life, over 1000 patents were issued to him or his associates; he was rightly known as 'the wizard of Menlo Park', a town in New Jersey where he set up his first 'invention factory'. Yet he was not really a scientist, having no theory or mathematics, and most of his success came from perfecting ideas or already existing inventions by the trial and error method. It was Edison who said that genius was one per cent inspiration and 99 per cent perspiration.

Edison's inquiring mind showed itself early in life. He was full of questions, and refused to accept anything unless he could test it for himself. This attitude, together with the fact that he was not good at mathematics, got him expelled from school with the remark from his teacher that his brain was 'addled'. Thereafter he was taught by his mother, a former schoolteacher herself.

By the age of ten, he had set up a chemical laboratory in the basement of his home. When he needed more money to buy supplies for his experiments, he went to work selling newspapers and confectionery on the Grand Trunk Railroad. By the time he was twelve, he had set up a laboratory and a printing press in a baggage car on a train, to continue his self-education and to make more money by selling his own paper.

He learned telegraphy on the railway, and his services as a telegrapher were in demand during the Civil War, when he travelled all over the country, incidentally studying electricity. In 1868 came his first invention: a machine to record votes in Congress. But Congress turned it down, because they were not interested in speeding up matters. Edison then resolved to work only on inventions that were commercially viable.

His first such invention was an improvement on the ticker machine which transmitted stock market prices. At this particular time in American history, when Wall Street was more powerful than the government and an enormous economic expansion was under way, this invention was so successful that Edison set up a small factory to build ticker-tape machines, which he later sold at a profit. This was the first instance of Edison's ability to see what needed to be invented before inventing it. Next he made improvements to the TELEGRAPH, culminating in a system which allowed four messages to be sent on one wire. He also made improvements to the TYPEWRITER.

By 1876 Edison was rich and famous. He quit manufacturing and set up his first 'invention factory', with a staff to help him develop ideas to a saleable state. Their first inventions were improvements to the TELEPHONE of Alexander Graham BELL, including a microphone. These inventions got Edison involved in the struggle over who was going to exploit Bell's invention, and established once and for all the concept of inventing to commercial order which has dominated twentieth century technology.

In 1877 Edison produced his most celebrated invention, certainly his own favourite. This was the phonograph. Edison's device used a tinfoil-covered drum which was hand cranked while a stylus traced a groove on it. The first recording ever made was of Edison's own voice reciting 'Mary Had a Little

Above right: Edison photographed in the early years of this century in the chemistry laboratory of his West Orange plant. It was here that he worked out a method of synthesizing carbolic acid.

B.

Right: Edison's first phonograph: hand cranked and with the cylinder covered in tinfoil as a recording surface.

MICHAEL HOLFORD LIBRARY

Lamb'. Typically, Edison had written out a list of ten uses for a sound recording machine before he built it; he saw it as a useful office machine, and did not foresee the multi-million-dollar record industry of today, which has survived competition from radio, television, and Edison's own motion pictures.

Improvements were immediately made on the phonograph by others. Phonograph companies were set up with reciprocal rights to patents. The groove on the cylinder was cut so that the varying depth of the groove represented the sound, the so-called 'hill-and-dale' method. Later, Emil Berliner built a device called the gramophone which cut the groove on a flat disc using a lateral method; that is, the sound was registered according to the sideways wiggle of the groove. Berliner's system was eventually adopted universally, but to this day the RECORD PLAYER is called the gramophone in Europe and the phonograph in the United States.

In 1878 Edison, using his trial and error method, began research towards the development of an incandescent LIGHT BULB. He made thousands of experiments before achieving success with a charred cotton thread, sealed in a vacuum so that it would glow without being consumed. His staff then worked out the principles of the modern generating and distributing system that made electric lights for every home practical. In 1882 the first generating station was opened at Pearl Street in New York. Edison used a direct current system; a former associate of his named Tesla developed an alternating current system for a rival company, Westinghouse, which eventually dominated. The Edison Electric Light Company, however, grew by mergers to become the General Electric Company.

While working on the light bulb, Edison made one of his few real scientific discoveries, the principle of the thermionic VALVE, or vacuum tube. At the time, however, there seemed to be no use for its properties; not until 1900 did J A FLEMING discover and develop its potential for wireless telegraphy.

He moved to a larger laboratory in West Orange, New Jersey, in 1887. In 1889 he built a motion picture camera and later set up a small studio for making films for peep-show machines. Once again however, the entertainment aspects of his invention did not really appeal to him, and it was finally left to others to develop the motion picture industry. He did not even bother to patent his motion picture camera design outside the United States, so that there were numerous infringements when imported machines appeared.

Edison's character was complex, and his reputation during his own lifetime was enormous. In 1896 Henry FORD went to Edison to ask his advice, and Edison told him that in his opinion the internal combustion engine was a practical source of power for a horseless carriage. Ford went on to develop the automobile industry, and idolized Edison for the rest of his life; Ford eventually built a restoration of one of Edison's laboratories on his estate in Michigan. In 1912 Edison would have been awarded the Nobel Prize with his former associate, Tesla, for their work on electrical generation and supply, but such was the animosity between them that Tesla refused to have his name linked with Edison's, and so neither won the award.

The flow of ideas continued until Edison's death in 1931.

PHOTRI

Above left: later phonograph cylinders were covered with wax, which gave a better sound quality.

Left: Edison's first light bulb, which used a carbon filament made by charring a cotton thread. The valve on the base is for exhausting air to create a vacuum inside the bulb.

EIDOPHOR

An eidophor is an extremely thin film of oil acted upon by an electric field to give its surface a controlled irregularity on a microscopic scale. This oil film is the basis of a complicated but ingenious system which can convert a TV signal into a display on a cinema screen—the word *eidophor* is Greek for 'image bearer'. It is very difficult to project a TV picture, because the original picture is created on the face of the picture tube by the phosphor screen being struck by electrons. There is no beam of light involved, and the intensity of illumination is quite low.

Working principles

In the eidophor projection system the incoming TV signal is amplified in the usual way and supplied to an electron gun, but instead of directing this at a phosphor-

Right : a colour eidophor projector. The three plated casings contain the electron gun assemblies, one for each colour. Each assembly has three units, so that if the gun in use fails another can be rotated into place within seconds. Above each gun is the projector lens for that colour; the same 2.5 kW lamp is used for all three systems.

Below : schematic diagram of a colour eidophor projector. The light from the lamp is split into three colours by a filter system similar to those in a colour TV camera, and each beam is then reflected on to the eidophor mirror. It may either be reflected straight back the way it came, or, if the electron beam is distorting the oil film, it will be reflected so as to miss the angled mirror slats. In that case it will be focused by the projector lens on to the main screen. A single beam is shown for each colour in this diagram.

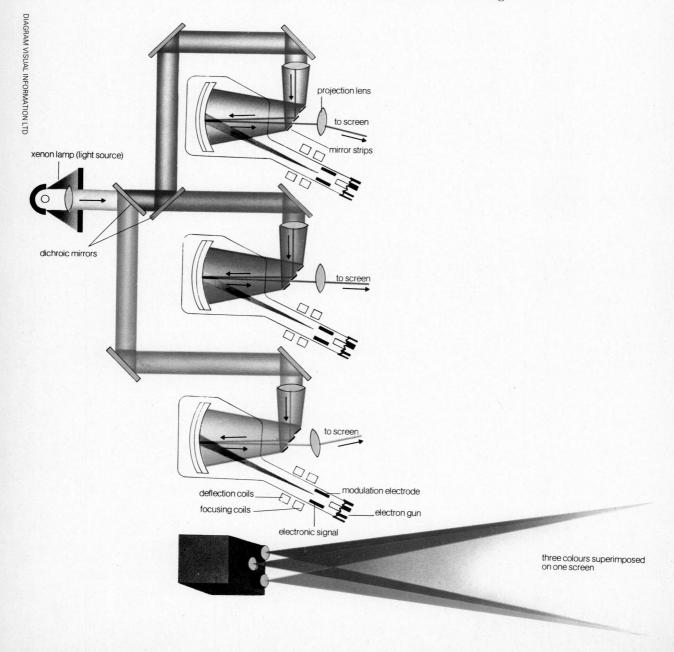

projection lens

to screen

mirror strips

xenon lamp (light source)

dichroic mirrors

to screen

to screen

deflection coils

focusing coils

modulation electrode

electron gun

electronic signal

three colours superimposed on one screen

coated screen it is aimed at the eidophor oil film. The electron bombardment creates local ELECTROSTATIC charges on the oil film, and these mutually repel each other to curve the film surface in a way that, in effect, converts the oil film into an extremely fine-grain lens or mirror (depending on whether the film is on a transparent glass plate or a reflecting surface) producing a duplicate of the TV picture. The film slowly rotates, so that the incident beam of electrons is always able to act on a fresh surface. Unlike a conventional TV system, the electron beam is not modified in intensity. Instead, it is focused or defocused by the signal strength: a bright spot on the image is represented by a sharply focused beam, giving maximum deflection of the surface. The film emerging from the electron beam gradually loses its charge and 'picture', but it is swept absolutely flat by a knife blade before it re-enters the beam. This flat surface gives no picture at all.

This unique fine-grain variable lens or mirror is thus able to serve as the controller for an extremely powerful beam of light which can be projected on the screen. There are different ways of doing this, but all involve a slatted screen or mirror which, as far as possible, arrests all light except that 'structured' by passing through, or being reflected by, the eidophor film.

A typical mirror has six slats, each about $\frac{1}{2}$ inch (13 mm) wide, arranged at 45° like the slats of a half-open venetian blind. The light source, invariably an ARC LAMP such as a xenon arc, is reflected off the angled slats on to the eidophor surface. It reflects back towards the slats in such a way that if there is no deflection of the beam by the eidophor, the light will be stopped by the slats. If, however, there is a slight deflection caused by the electron beam, the light will not be interrupted by the slats and will pass through a projection lens on to the screen. This screen may be as large as 30 × 40 ft (9 × 12 m)—as in a cinema.

Colour pictures A normal colour TV set uses three electron guns, aimed at red, green and blue phosphors on the TV screen. Three separate electron guns and eidophors are used in the large-screen system, again each dealing with an image which is to be projected in one colour only. To avoid problems of matching up three light sources, only one arc lamp is used, but its light is split into the three colours by a system of dichroic optical FILTERS. These beams are then reflected on to their respective eidophors and recombine on the screen to give a full colour picture.

The eidophor is just one of several ways of producing a large picture display controlled by a TV signal, the output of a computer or some other dynamic source. Such a picture, to be useful, must change in 'real time'; that is it must faithfully reproduce the incoming signal and must not lag behind. The eidophor has the great advantage of being capable of electronic control in the purest sense, in that the controlling medium is a beam of free electrons. On the other hand, this means that the central portion of the equipment must be sealed and operated under a high vacuum. Developments of the eidophor are aimed at greater simplicity and the ability to operate at ordinary atmospheric pressure. Broad research programmes are trying to perfect rival schemes such as electroluminescent displays, displays using LIQUID CRYSTALS, solid state light systems (mostly based upon various kinds of LED, light emitting diode) and displays generated by fibre optics.

Left: the big screen TV system in operation. It has many uses, from the televising of sporting events to operations and conferences, where it may replace the traditional blackboards and projectors.

EINSTEIN, Albert (1879–1955)

Albert Einstein, the theoretical physicist famous for his theory of RELATIVITY, was born in 1879 at Ulm, Germany, to parents of German-Jewish descent. His early education, at first in Munich and later in Switzerland, did not mark him out as any kind of genius at all. He found the pedantic methods of the German education system totally uninteresting, and he used often to miss lessons in order to indulge his voracious appetite for reading. At 17, he entered the Swiss Federal Polytechnic in Zürich after rapid cramming of a subject he had somewhat neglected—mathematics. The more liberal and easygoing atmosphere of Switzerland was much more in keeping with his own reflective ways, and in 1901 after graduating, he took out Swiss citizenship. Years later, in the winter of 1932–3, while Einstein was on a fortuitous visit to the California Institute of Technology, Hitler came to power in Europe, and Einstein decided to stay on in the United States, becoming an American citizen in 1940.

He had entered the Polytechnic with the idea of becoming a teacher but had difficulty in finding a post and ended up in the patent office in Berne. In 1905 he received his doctorate in physics from the University of Zürich. That year saw the publication of three of his papers, any one of which would have earned him a doctorate. Unfortunately, many of his ideas were only intelligible to a small minority of physicists and recognition did not come immediately.

In each of these papers, however, Einstein had managed to

Below: Professor Albert Einstein, photographed in December 1934, delivering a lecture at the American Association for the Advancement of Science at the Carnegie Institute of Technology.

combine the principle of sound empirical science—that any explanation must make as few unproven assumptions as possible—with an acute insight of new ideas. One of these papers was on the Special Theory of relativity, which was to appear in its final form in 1915 as his General Theory of relativity. It literally overturned the then accepted basis of physics. Experiments measuring the speed of light had shown its speed to be exactly the same whether the source was moving away from or towards the observer. This was, however, a contradiction of Newtonian mechanics.

This paradox was resolved by Einstein's Special Theory. It involved, however, a new interpretation of mechanics, which resulted in the essential equivalence of mass and energy. Matter, said Einstein, was a form of energy, and energy a form of matter, with their interrelationship expressed by the famous equation $E = mc^2$, where E = energy, m = mass, and c^2 = the square of the speed of light. When a minuscule amount of mass is annihilated, it is replaced by an immense amount of energy: this is the principle behind atomic energy.

The other papers published in 1905 dealt with his explanations of the photoelectric effect, for which he was awarded the Nobel Prize in 1922, and of Brownian motion. The former was a turning point in modern physics. It not only provided the first clear and qualitative account of the ionization of metals by a beam of light, but it also showed that light came in discrete 'packets', which he called photons. Light was therefore shown to be 'quantized', just as matter was known to be. Five years previously Niels Bohr had shown a similar quantizing of the energy of the electrons in the atom, and so the stage was now set for the development of the QUANTUM THEORY. Relativity and the quantum theory are two of the most important

contributions to twentieth-century physics.

Brownian motion, the small zigzagging movements executed by dust particles immersed in a fluid, had baffled scientists since its discovery by the Scottish botanist Robert Brown in the nineteenth century. Einstein's paper explained it in terms of the millions of collisions that take place between the molecules of the fluid and immersed microscopic particles. This also had important ramifications for the advancement of physics, for it was the first occasion that the atomic theory was shown capable of producing explanations of observed phenomena.

Einstein spent the following years working through his conceptions of space and time, supporting himself and his family in a number of teaching posts in various European universities. After teaching at the University of Berne he moved, in 1909, to the University of Zürich and in 1910 to the German University of Prague, returning to the Swiss Polytechnic in Zürich in 1912. Finally in 1913 he settled in Berlin to become a professor at the University of Berlin and a member of the research institute, the Royal Prussian Academy of Sciences, as well as a director of the prestigious Kaiser Wilhelm Institute. While there, his General Theory of relativity was published. This work, of enormous intellectual and philosophical elegance, developed the concepts he had outlined in the Special Theory into a new interpretation of the Universe. In it, the laws of physics were reduced to those of the geometry of a space-time continuum. It related gravitation with electromagnetics, two fundamental forces of the Universe that had been hitherto treated as distinct entities. The first proof of his theory came shortly afterwards, when it was observed during an eclipse of the Sun that the light from distant stars is bent as it passes close to the gravitational pull of the Sun.

In his personal attitudes Einstein reflected the growing realization within the scientific community that the scientist, by virtue of both his intellect and the nature of his discoveries, has a special responsibility towards society. World War 1 affected him deeply, and made him very conscious of the outside world and the social injustice and folly that abounds there. Yet he was too much of a genius to ever live completely outside the rarefied atmosphere of his own mind. He was notoriously absent-minded, and anecdotes about him are to be found in abundance in his biographies. One day, for example, a student pointed out to him that he had forgotten to put on any socks. Einstein observed that, since he had not noticed it beforehand, socks must be a quite expendable article of clothing. From that day he is supposed never to have worn socks.

In 1921 he visited America to speak on behalf of the Zionist cause, and in 1922 he was appointed to the Intellectual Co-operation arm of the League of Nations. When it became known in 1939 that German scientists were working on the FISSION process that would lead to the construction of an A-BOMB, he wrote his now famous letter to President Roosevelt. As a result of this, the Manhattan Project was set up, which resulted in the development of the atomic bomb by the Americans before the Germans. He was deeply involved throughout the war in organizations providing relief for refugees from war-torn Europe. He died at Princeton, New Jersey in 1955.

Perhaps the best epitaph for him is the German proverb he was fond of quoting to express his own convictions about the world, 'God is subtle, but he is not malicious'.

Below: Albert Einstein holding an informal seminar at the Institute of Advanced Learning.

EJECTION SEAT

Towards the end of World War 2 emergency parachute escapes from military aircraft were becoming increasingly difficult, and the introduction of jet-powered aircraft with their vastly increased speed virtually eliminated the possibility of a successful 'over the side' bale-out.

In 1944 Mr James Martin (now Sir James Martin) was invited by the then Ministry of Aircraft Production in London to investigate the practicability of providing fighter aircraft with a means of assisted escape for the pilot in an emergency.

After investigating alternative schemes it soon became apparent that this could be best achieved by forced ejection of the pilot's seat, with the pilot sitting in it, and that the most effective way of doing this would be by an explosive charge. After ejection, the pilot would fall away from the seat and open his PARACHUTE by pulling a ripcord in the usual way. This also fitted in with Air Staff requirements at that time, that any ejection system should 'utilize existing safety equipment'.

Operation When an ejection seat is operated in an emergency, the seat, complete with the occupant and carrying a parachute and a pack of survival aids, is ejected from the aircraft by an ejection gun. The ejection gun is secured to the aircraft vertically behind the back of the seat, and is powerful enough

Below: a training rig for teaching pilots how to use an ejection seat. The pilot is strapped into an ejection seat inside the dummy cockpit, and when the seat is operated it travels on rails up the front of the tower. This picture was taken in 1949 at Chivenor, Devon.

to hurl the seat well clear of the aircraft even if it is travelling at high speed, possibly faster than the speed of sound.

Some seats are fitted with a rocket motor underneath the seat in addition to the ejection gun to increase the height attained by the seat. The rocket is fired as the seat leaves the aircraft and the combined force of the gun and the rocket will propel the seat and occupant to a height of about 300 ft (91 m), which is high enough to allow a parachute to open fully, even if the ejection is made from ground level with aircraft stationary. This feature is a decided asset when installed in modern vertical take-off and short take-off aircraft, and also in conventional aircraft should ejection be necessary with the aircraft in a nose-down attitude at speed near the ground.

To commence ejection, the pilot pulls on a handle located above his head or between his knees, or pulls a screen down over his face which starts the ejection sequence and also protects his face from the air blast. This jettisons the cockpit canopy and fires a cartridge which ignites other cartridges in the gun and, if fitted, the rocket motor, which then provide the thrust to eject the seat.

After the seat has left the aircraft, a *drogue* (small parachute) attached to the top of the seat is deployed. To ensure quick and positive deployment of the drogue, it is pulled out of its container at the top of the seat with some force by a heavy 'billet' fired from a drogue gun. The object of the drogue is to stabilize the seat and slow it down to a speed at which the occupant's parachute can be opened without fear of it bursting.

When the drogue has slowed the seat sufficiently, a barostatic-

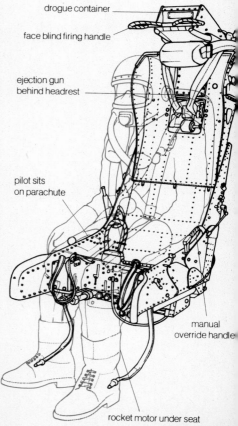

drogue container

face blind firing handle

ejection gun behind headrest

pilot sits on parachute

manual override handle

rocket motor under seat

DIAGRAM VISUAL INFORMATION LTD

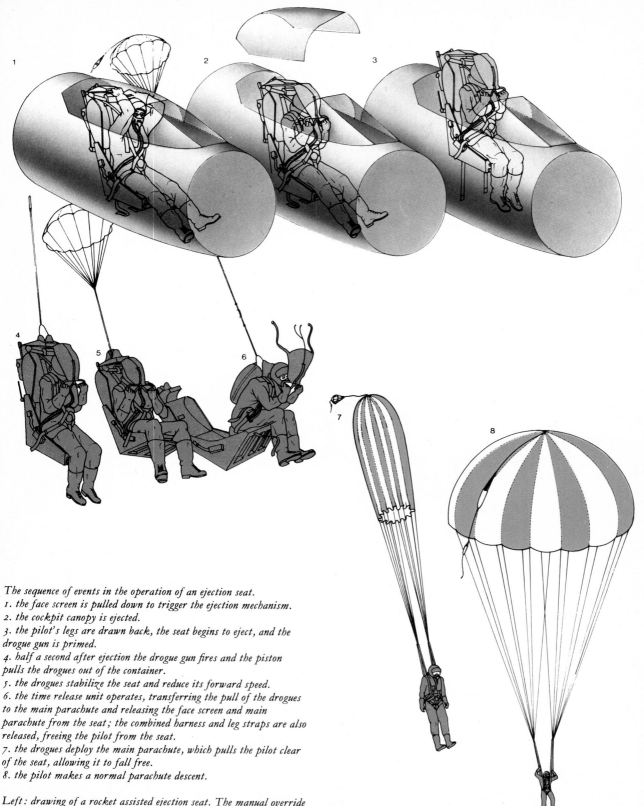

The sequence of events in the operation of an ejection seat.
1. the face screen is pulled down to trigger the ejection mechanism.
2. the cockpit canopy is ejected.
3. the pilot's legs are drawn back, the seat begins to eject, and the drogue gun is primed.
4. half a second after ejection the drogue gun fires and the piston pulls the drogues out of the container.
5. the drogues stabilize the seat and reduce its forward speed.
6. the time release unit operates, transferring the pull of the drogues to the main parachute and releasing the face screen and main parachute from the seat; the combined harness and leg straps are also released, freeing the pilot from the seat.
7. the drogues deploy the main parachute, which pulls the pilot clear of the seat, allowing it to fall free.
8. the pilot makes a normal parachute descent.

Left: drawing of a rocket assisted ejection seat. The manual override handle allows the pilot, if necessary, to deploy the main parachute and separate from the seat before the time release unit has operated.

ally controlled (pressure sensitive) time release unit releases the drogue from the top of the seat, transferring its pull to the canopy of the occupant's parachute, pulling it out of its pack. Simultaneously the time-release unit releases the occupant's safety harness from the seat, and the occupant is pulled clear by his opening parachute to make a normal parachute descent while his seat falls free.

Should the ejection take place above 10,000 ft (3048 m), the action of the time-release unit is delayed by the barostat control which responds to atmospheric pressure in a similar way to an aneroid altimeter or BAROMETER. (Atmospheric pressure falls as the altitude increases.) By delaying the opening of the main parachute until this height, the seat and its occupant, stabilized by the drogue, descend quickly through the cold, rarefied upper atmosphere. The seat incorporates a built-in oxygen supply for the occupant to breathe, which is turned on automatically during ejection.

This entire sequence is automatically controlled from the time the pilot operates the seat until he lands by parachute, but in the unlikely event of the mechanism failing the pilot can intervene and open his parachute by a manual ripcord.

Escape capsules   The use of an ordinary ejection seat is impractical for escapes from aircraft flying at speeds greatly in excess of the speed of sound, as the pilot will be subjected to extremely high and potentially dangerous deceleration forces as he leaves the plane. The force of the air against the pilot could in fact be so high as to tear away his clothing, helmet, and breathing apparatus. To overcome this difficulty, modern supersonic fighters and bombers may be built so that the cockpit section is in the form of a self-contained pressurized capsule which in an emergency can be separated from the fuselage of the aircraft by explosive bolts and rocket motors. The capsule has parachutes to slow it and stabilize it, and may be fitted with ejection seats so that its occupants can separate from it when a safe velocity and altitude have been reached.

Survival aids   In addition to his parachute, a pilot usually has a pack containing a variety of aids to assist survival should he land in a hostile or unfriendly environment.

If he comes down in a lake or the sea a self-inflating rubber life-raft is used, in addition to his normal lifejacket. Of his other survival aids the most important is a radio beacon which sends out a distress signal enabling search aircraft and ships to locate him. Signalling equipment, protective clothing, food and fishing equipment are also contained in the survival pack.

The ejection seat is one of the most important parts of a modern military aircraft, and one make alone, the Martin-Baker, has saved over 3400 lives to date.

Below: a picture of a pilot ejecting from a Hawker Siddeley 'Harrier' jet fighter, using a rocket propelled ejection seat.

ELASTICITY

No solid material is completely inflexible and all will 'yield' to a certain extent when a force is applied to them. This yield may be described as a change in size, shape or volume, depending on the body in question and the nature of the force exerted on it. If, however, the body returns to its original size, shape or volume when the force is removed, it is said to be *elastic*.

This property of elasticity is possessed by all solids and liquids to different degrees, but always within certain limits. This limit is called the *elastic limit* of the material and if the material is forced to yield beyond this limit it no longer behaves in an elastic manner. In solids, the material becomes permanently deformed (when a large force is applied) through a process known as *plastic deformation*. When the force is removed the material will not return to its original size or shape and the overall behaviour is *inelastic*. The elastic properties of materials have important consequences in engineering, and must be considered, for example, in bridge and building designs.

Hooke's law Robert HOOKE (1635–1703) was the first to study seriously this property in solids and the outcome of his research is known as Hooke's law. This states that within the elastic limit of a body, the change in length is proportional to the force acting on the body producing this change. In more general terms, *extension* is proportional to *tension*.

For example, if a steel wire is firmly fixed to a solid beam and a weight attached to the lower end, then the wire is stretched by a certain amount. Doubling the weight doubles the stretch, and this holds until the elastic limit is reached.

Stress, strain and elastic modulus As extension is proportional to tension, the ratio of tension to extension is a constant. This constant is, however, not only dependent on the material but also on the shape. This is unfortunate as it 'hides' the intrinsic elasticity of the material itself. To overcome this, it is necessary to replace tension by *stress* and extension by *strain*. Like tension and extension, the ratio of stress to strain is also a constant, but it is a constant of the material alone called the *elastic modulus* or *modulus of elasticity*.

Longitudinal stress and strain When the force producing a change in length acts along a body (such as a beam), the corresponding stresses and strains are longitudinal and the particular elastic modulus used in these situations is called the *stretch modulus* or *Young's modulus*.

If two steel wires of the same length and material but different thickness (cross-sectional area) are fixed to a beam and equal weights attached to their lower ends then the thinner wire will be stretched most. The reason for this is that the force per unit area of the wire's cross-section is greater for the thin wire than for the thick. This ratio of force to cross-sectional area is called the *stress* and has the units of pressure—such as pounds per square inch (psi) or newtons per square metre (N/m^2). If a body

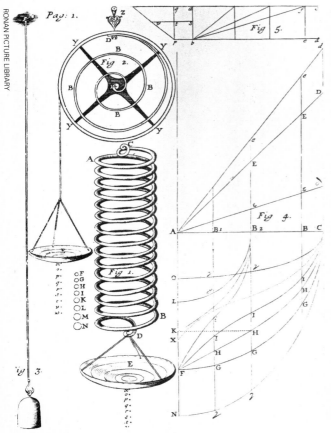

Above: these drawings are from Robert Hooke's experiments on spiral springs, published in 1678 in his book 'De Potentia Restitutiva' (the power of elasticity). From these experiments 'Hooke's law' was deduced.

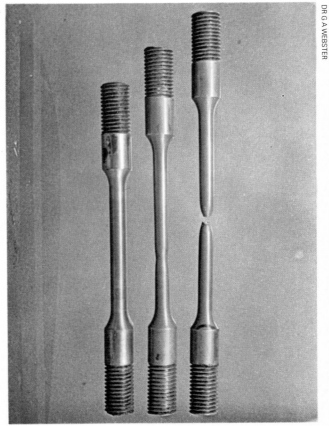

Above: what happens when a material is stretched beyond its elastic limit. The bar at the left is the original bar before stretching. With a tensioning load applied, the material stretches in an elastic manner, but beyond a certain load necking occurs leading to fracture.

DIAGRAM VISUAL INFORMATION LTD

is in tension it is said to undergo a *tensile* stress and in compression, a *compressive* stress.

If the two steel wires of the previous example are of the same thickness but different length, then the longer wire is extended most. The ratio of extension to original length is in both cases, however, the same. This ratio is called the *tensile strain* and it is the relative change in length. Strain is a dimensionless quantity as it is extension (length) divided by (the original) length.

The ratio of tensile stress to tensile strain in this example is Young's modulus for steel and the same figure would occur in a compression test for compressive stress and strain.

In engineering, Young's modulus is important when choosing a material to undergo tensile and compressive loads. For example, when designing a bridge it is important to know how much the beams will yield under longitudinal loads and Young's modulus of the particular material will be used.

Shear stress and strain

Another kind of elasticity is encountered when things bend. The elastic modulus relating to bending is the *shear modulus*, *rigidity modulus* or *torsion modulus*.

If, for example, one end of a steel rod is firmly fixed to a horizontal base and a horizontal force applied to the top surface (that is, a *shear force*), the rod will bend, or lean over, slightly. In this case, the rod does not change in size but in shape—it distorts. This shearing force produces a *shear stress* in the steel which is the force divided by the area over which the force acts (that is, the top surface of the rod which is therefore its cross-sectional area). The *shear strain* is a measure of the distortion of the rod and is determined from the angle of lean. The shear modulus is calculated from the ratio of shear stress to shear strain.

Shear modulus is used to calculate the degree of yield when, for example, a horizontal beam is loaded with weights.

Bulk modulus

When considering the change in volume of a solid or liquid under pressure, the bulk modulus is used. This is defined as the ratio of pressure (stress) to the relative change in volume (*volumetric strain*). Bulk modulus is an important factor to consider, for example, in hydraulic systems.

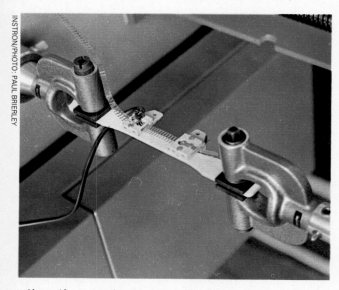

Above: if a material is forced beyond its elastic limit, it no longer behaves in an elastic manner. Firstly, the material is deformed—in a tension test this leads to 'necking' where the material 'thins out' at its weakest point. Finally it will break or 'fracture'.

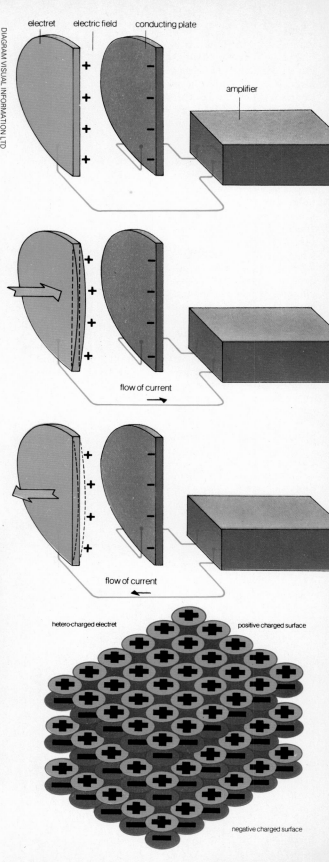

electret   electric field   conducting plate

amplifier

flow of current

flow of current

hetero-charged electret   positive charged surface

negative charged surface

ELECTRET

An electret is an insulating material (or dielectric) which retains an ELECTROSTATIC charge for many years and as such can be considered the electrostatic equivalent of a permanent magnet. Thus, while the magnet is a permanent source of external magnetic field, the electret is a permanent source of electric field. Electrets are usually produced in sheet or film form with one surface positively charged and the other negatively charged.

The analogy between magnets and electrets can be taken further because both lose their effects when heated. Furthermore, a magnet will retain its magnetization longer if the magnetic path is 'short circuited' between the north and south poles with a 'bridge' of iron, and similarly an electret will retain its charge longer if the two surfaces are electrically short circuited by sandwiching between two connected metal plates or 'keepers'.

Electrical polarization When an electret is formed, the material is said to be polarized—meaning that the charges have been orientated in a preferred direction. This polarization can involve either *heterocharges* or *homocharges* or both, depending on the material used and the method of preparation.

When the charges are arranged in positive–negative pairs and aligned in the same direction throughout the material it is said to be *heterocharged*. Here the arrangement is the same as the dipoles created in the dielectric material of a capacitor (see CAPACITANCE). Heterocharge and dipole mean the same thing in this context, but the dipoles set up in the dielectric of a capacitor are only a temporary phenomenon associated with the voltage across the capacitor plates.

When individual charges collect on the surface of the electret material it is said to be *homocharged*. Here, charges of the same

Below: electrets can be heterocharged with the charges arranged in positive-negative pairs or homocharged with the charges on the surface only. Left: in a microphone and amplifier circuit the electret material and metal marker plate are connected as shown. When the electret is moved towards the marker plate an induced current flows through the amplifier input circuitry, producing a voltage.

Right: this compact electret microphone contains an electret transducer connected to a small high input impedance high gain amplifier with battery. The frequency response is 40 to 18,000 Hz.

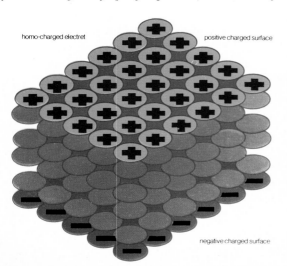

homo-charged electret · positive charged surface

negative charged surface

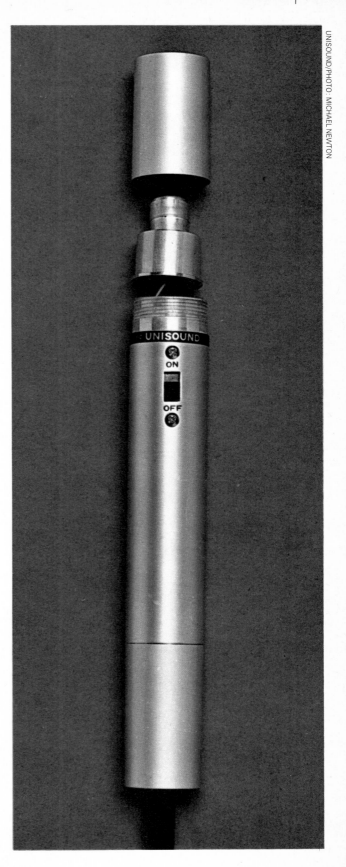

kind are 'fixed' in one surface with the opposite charges on the other surface.

Forming electrets

The earliest electrets were formed by a Japanese, Eguchi, in 1919. He found that if a high voltage was applied to two electrodes immersed in a molten mixture of waxes and resins and the mixture was then solidified with the voltage on, the material between the electrodes retained some permanent 'frozen' polarization. This technique is known as the *thermoelectret* forming process and has been extended to include forming from materials requiring only elevated temperatures (not necessarily to the molten state). Indeed, in some cases no thermal treatment is required at all.

The most common material used for early work was carnauba wax, a hard yellow Brazilian wax used in furniture polishes and cosmetics. Electrets have been formed in this way from materials including 'Perspex' ['Plexiglas'], ice, shellac and anthracene, and many other solid dielectrics (insulators) can be polarized.

More recently interest has centred on the production of homocharged-only electrets, where in essence the effect is simply the ability of some materials to retain surface *electrostatic charge* for considerable periods. This renewed interest coincided with the advent of pure polymers in flexible film form. They retain charge for long periods and because of their very good insulating properties and roll film form, permit simpler continuous charging techniques such as knife edge 'corona' charging and electron beam charging. Electrets of this type have been made from polyethylene, polypropylene, polystyrene, polycarbonate, fluorocarbon (including PTFE—'Teflon') and many other polymer films.

Uses

One of the earliest uses of carnauba thermoelectrets was by the Japanese in the MICROPHONES of some of their field telephones during World War 2. At the same time British and US patents were taken out for their use in microphones, loudspeakers, electrometers and voltmeters.

With the development of suitable polymer films, the interest in electrets for microphone use was renewed in the 1960s. The polymer film electret can form the flexible diaphragm of a condenser microphone without the need of an external polarizing voltage. Such microphones have the advantage of wide, flat frequency responses, low distortion, insensitivity to shock and 'noise', cheapness and lightness, and can be made extremely small (less than 0.2 inch (0.5 cm) in diameter and thickness).

Other forms of electret foil TRANSDUCERS have been used for ultrasonic detectors (up to 10^8 Hz), seismic detectors (down to 10^{-3} Hz on Apollo missions) and all frequencies between, including record player pickups, hearing aids and earphones. Another application is in push button 'keys' for such devices as telephones and electronic calculators. It is estimated that ten million electret transducers are produced annually in Japan alone.

Electret transducers

In the basic arrangement of all electret transducers, a flexible electret diaphragm is coated on one surface with a very thin metallic film. Facing the uncoated surface, but not touching it, is a metal plate. Electrical leads are attached to the metallic film and the plate and taken to the input of a high gain AMPLIFIER. When the diaphragm is moved the induced charge on the metal plate changes, meaning that a current flows in the amplifier input circuit. This, in turn, produces a voltage across the input terminals which is amplified by the amplifier.

ELECTRIC ARC (see arc light)

ELECTRIC CELL (see battery)

ELECTRICITY

Electricity, as its name suggests, is intimately bound up with the properties and consequent behaviour of the ELECTRON. The charge on the electron and its relatively high mobility, the ease with which it can be caused to move, are its most important properties from the point of view of electricity. It is the motion of electrons that lies at the root of all electrical phenomena, as, for example, in a current in an electric CIRCUIT.

Electrons are found in all ATOMS, surrounding the compact core, or nucleus, of protons and neutrons in orbital layers or 'shells'. The ELECTROSTATIC attraction between the protons and electrons holds the atom together. The electrons in the outermost shell, which are often termed the VALENCY electrons (those which take part in chemical BOND formation), are only weakly bound to the nucleus in many atoms. This is especially the case with the valency electrons of the atoms of the metallic elements, such as copper, silver, and sodium. The weakness of the attraction, combined with the fact that the mass of both the proton and the neutron is each nearly two thousand times that of the electron, means that the valency electrons can be relatively easily moved. Since electrons are present in all atoms, electricity, broadly defined, is found in many forms throughout nature. *Photo-electricity*, the movement of electrons from their atomic

Below : demonstrations of electrical phenomena were popular in 18th century France. Here Abbé Nollet (1700–1770), an associate of du Fay, is demonstrating the effects of static electricity.

Bottom : von Guericke discovered, in the 1660s, that an electrical charge could be produced by rubbing a rotating globe of sulphur. This machine, devised by G M Bose, used a globe of glass.

THE MANSELL COLLECTION

THE BETTMANN ARCHIVE

levels by the action of light, and the whole field of *electro-chemistry* (see ELECTROLYSIS) are examples of the extent to which the effects of the electron's properties are encountered.

Current When the atoms or molecules of an element or compound come together, they arrange themselves in a regular array termed the CRYSTAL lattice. The type of crystal lattice and the mobility that it allows the valency electrons, and the nature of the particular atom itself, largely determines the electrical properties of the element or compound. RESISTANCE, for example, is a measure of the amount of energy expended by the electrons in moving against the opposition of the atoms in the lattice. This expended energy appears mostly in the familiar form of heat. CAPACITORS exploit the low electron mobility of insulators to build up a surplus of electrons on one of their plates and a deficiency on the other. This imbalance of charge can later be 'discharged' in a short pulse of current.

The lattices of metallic elements allow the valency electrons a high degree of freedom and present little opposition to their motion. As a result, they are excellent conductors of electrical current. Insulators, on the other hand, are characterized by the low mobility their atoms and lattices allow the valency electrons (see CONDUCTION, electric).

The crucial importance of the type of crystal lattice is demonstrated by the case of the two distinct crystalline forms, or allotropes, of pure carbon. In the graphite form, carbon is an excellent conductor, but in the diamond form it is a poor conductor. The atoms making up the two lattices are exactly the same, but the electron mobilities allowed by the lattice types are completely different.

Individual electrons move along solid conductors in a random 'shunting' manner; it takes a flow of over six million million million electrons per second to make a current of one *ampere*, named after the French physicist A M AMPÈRE. While the effects of a current (such as ELECTROMAGNETIC RADIATION) are transmitted with the speed of light, each electron is only drifting in the direction of the current at an effective rate of around one inch per second (2.54 cm per sec). When *ionic compounds*, such as common salt (NaCl), are dissolved in water, the water molecules cause the sodium and the chlorine atoms to split up, or 'dissociate', into free IONS. The negative chloride ion, which carries the single valency electron in the outer shell of the sodium atom, and the correspondingly positive sodium ion are then able to carry a current through the solution. Instead of the mobility of the electron, it is the mobility of the ions through the solvent (in this case water) that determines the resistance of the solution.

Voltage Although the electrostatic attraction between the proton and the electron is one of the fundamental forces of the Universe, the systematic motion of electrons that constitutes a current is not directly caused by it. Current flows between points of 'potential difference', this difference being expressed in *volts*. The voltage between two points is a measure of the energy an electron gains in moving them: the electrons move because it is preferable for them to do so, and the energy arises

Below left: lack of knowledge made many early electrical experiments dangerous and unpredictable. This engraving shows George Richmann after he was struck by lightning during an experiment.

Below right: another of Abbé Nollet's experiments, investigating the effects of high voltage electricity on plants and animals. The electricity was conducted along the chain supporting the specimens.

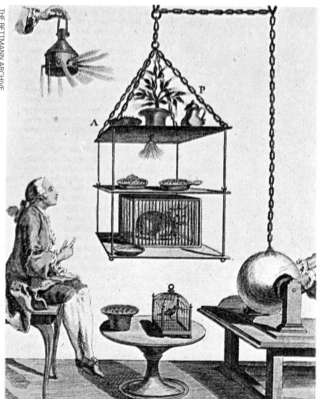

as a result of the 'energy levels' the electron can fill in the atom.

The complete theory of electricity, which clearly hinges around the atomic and QUANTUM theories of matter, has only evolved during this century. But the scientific observation of electrical phenomena, and even their exploitation in practical applications such as the BATTERY, long preceded this full understanding. This is another example of a common occurrence in science: the laws of nature have often been put to good use even though the principles underlying them were either unknown or misunderstood.

Triboelectrification The first record of the study of electricity can be found as early as the sixth century BC. A Greek, Thales of Miletus (624–548 BC), observed that when certain substances were rubbed they were able, for a time, to attract light objects. Most people are familiar with this phe-

nomenon in one form or another: the effect a dry nylon comb has on hair, making it stand on end, is one example. Also when the plastic body of a fountain pen is rubbed with a silk, cotton, or woollen cloth, it can pick up small pieces of paper. This is called *triboelectrification*, and it is one of the most fundamental results of the electrical properties of matter.

The triboelectrification of an object is due to the frictional force applied in the rubbing process. Certain types of atoms can be ionized like this, being either partially stripped of their valency electrons or given some of the valency electrons of another atom. The cloth that is used to induce this ionization,

Below : a sheet of 'Perspex' was charged up by scanning a high energy beam of electrons across it, and when it was earthed (grounded) at one edge this spectacular discharge pattern occurred.

STL/ITT/PHOTO: PAUL BRIERLEY

as could be expected, is also ionized—with the opposite charge. It, too, has the ability to attract light objects for a while. This ionization, however, is not at all extensive, and the normal balance of positive and negative charge is soon restored when the object is 'earthed' [grounded]. This can be done by the action of the moisture in the surrounding air or by being simply touched.

Magnetism and polarity

The word 'electron' is actually derived from the Greek word for the natural resin amber, *elektron*. Amber was one of the first substances to be triboelectrified. The Greeks connected this phenomenon with

Below: the 'flashover' discharge created during the testing of a high voltage insulator, of the type used in power stations, transforming stations and switching compounds.

magnetism, which they had observed between pieces of magnetite ore. Since both this force of electrostatic attraction and the force of magnetism act 'at a distance'—that is, do not require any physical contact to pull objects together—they seemed to fall into one class. Thus, from the outset, the scientific studies of electricity and magnetism were linked, although for a spurious reason. The first genuine connections between the two were not made until 1820, when Oersted chanced to see that a COMPASS needle was deflected by the presence of a current-carrying wire. Strangely enough, one school of Greek thought did develop a simple version of the atomic theory, (see EPICURUS) but the link between electricity and the atom did not come until the turn of this century.

In 1551 Jerome Cardan studied the similarities and differences between magnetic and electrostatic attraction. He proposed

REYROLLE PARSON LTD

that electricity or, rather, the triboelectric aspect of it that he was concerned with, was a type of fluid. All things considered, it is not such a bad model. What was more important, it meant that this mysterious force was now treated as something quite material and not at all magical. Fluid theories of electricity became popular in the 18th and early 19th centuries.

In 1600 William Gilbert, an early investigator into electrical and magnetic phenomena, conducted extensive experiments into triboelectrification. He classified substances into good or poor electrifiers, depending on how easy it was to induce in them this ability to attract light objects. His classifications can be seen to correspond to the modern ones of 'insulators' and 'conductors' respectively.

The fluid theories of electricity were subsequently developed further by the French scientist du Fay. In 1733 he proposed that there was only one fluid responsible. In 1747 Benjamin FRANKLIN, in his celebrated experiments with kites flown during thunderstorms and an early type of capacitor called a Leyden jar, proposed that there were two types of electrical fluid. One was responsible for 'positive', the other for 'negative' electrification.

This distinction between positive and negative came about because some electrified substances attracted each other, whereas others were repelled by them. This again is another obvious parallel with magnetism: a north pole of a magnet repels another north pole, just as a south pole repels another south pole, but a north pole and a south pole attract each other. The fluid theories, however, were subsequently discarded with the advances in scientific knowledge in the 19th century, but the 'positive' and 'negative' terminology was retained, along with the 'like repels, unlike attracts' rule.

Coulomb's law

The quantitative development of electrical theory began in the second half of the 18th century. The independent discovery, by Priestley in 1767 and COULOMB in 1785, of the so called Coulomb law, and its exact expression in a mathematical formula, started it. The Coulomb law is to electricity what NEWTON'S LAW of gravitation is to physics, and in fact it is remarkably similar in its general form.

Coulomb's law relates the electrostatic force of attraction or repulsion between two groups of charge to the amount of charge, the distance separating them, and the medium in which they are situated. The force was found to vary with the reciprocal of the square of the distance between the charges. This means that doubling the separation will reduce the force to one quarter of its original magnitude. The electrostatic force is thus a 'short-range' force, as it dies away in intensity very rapidly with distance. This formula has stood essentially unchanged to this day, a tribute to the experimental precision of both scientists.

From then on the understanding of electricity broadened rapidly, due mainly to the invention of the first reliable source of continuous current. This was called the 'voltaic pile', and it is the forerunner of the modern battery. In fact, it relied on the same current-generating process as the modern battery—the controlled electrolytic action of a weakly acidic solution on metals. Its invention in 1800 by the Italian physicist Alessandro VOLTA, after whom the 'volt' is named, was a turning point in the study of electricity. Before the voltaic pile, the only way of 'storing' charge was a bank of electroscopes (devices

for storing electrostatic charges), the current from which was small and usually too short-lived to allow its effects to be studied in any detail. The electroscopes were each laboriously 'charged' by repeatedly transferring the charge from a triboelectrified substance such as amber or glass on to the electroscope.

Electromagnetism

The chance discovery of the relationship between magnetism and an electrical current by Oersted in 1820 was the next breakthrough. The brilliant British physicist Michael FARADAY soon after discovered that the relationship was two way. Not only does the motion of charge that takes place in a current produce a magnetic field in its vicinity but, conversely, the 'motion' of a magnetic field produces a current. In 1831 he showed that the continuous variation of the magnetic field, or 'flux', passing through a conducting wire loop causes a current to be circulated in the loop. The mutual dependence of electricity and magnetism is the principle behind what is now termed INDUCTANCE.

In 1851 Faraday realized that it is not just the actual motion of the electrons that lies at the centre of electricity. Rather, it is the electric and magnetic 'force fields' they set up as they move along. In 1865 James Clerk MAXWELL published his theory

Right: lightning is the most spectacular natural form of electricity, produced by the discharge of electricity between highly charged clouds and the earth. This picture was taken at Santa Fé, New Mexico.

SUSAN GRIGGS AGENCY / ADAM WOOLFITT

of electromagnetism, which related the two in an exact, mathematical fashion.

The rapid development of the atomic theory, with its discovery that all matter is ultimately composed of, among other particles, electrons, meant that electricity was afforded a central role in physics. In 1887 Hertz showed that light was merely a travelling electromagnetic wave, and thus optics was seen to be basically a branch of electrical theory. When J J Thomson provided the first positive demonstration of the existence of the electron in 1897, the ancient enigma of electricity was finally explained.

During this century, both an understanding of the fundamental, atomic-level principles of electricity and the development of its applications have increased dramatically. For example, the ability to generate large quantities of electrical power, such as through the 'harnessing' of running water for hydroelectric power, and the solution of the related problems of its wide-scale distribution, has brought vast changes in the standard of living. The invention of thermionic vacuum devices such as VALVES [vacuum tubes], and the more recent work on SEMICONDUCTORS, has opened up the science of ELECTRONICS.

ELECTRICITY SUPPLY (see power supply)

ELECTRIC MOTOR

An electric motor is more properly described as an 'electric machine' for the same piece of apparatus can be used *either* as a motor *or* as a generator of electricity. There is no type of machine which can convert electrical energy into mechanical energy, which cannot convert in the opposite direction if so required.

All types of electric motor use the principles of ELECTRO-MAGNETISM in which *either* electric currents flowing in wires situated in a magnetic field experience mechanical force *or* in which electromagnets apply force to a ferromagnetic (intrinsically highly magnetic) material. The electric current used by motors can be either direct current (DC) as obtained from a battery, or alternating current (AC) which is generally more convenient to use, mainly because the supply voltage can be raised or lowered so effectively by static TRANSFORMERS.

Electric motors usually produce rotational motion which is directly applicable to mechanical systems with wheels. The various types of motor can be classified into two groups: 'electromagnetic' machines and 'magnetic' machines. The electromagnetic group includes induction, synchronous, DC, AC polyphase commutator, single-phase AC commutator and

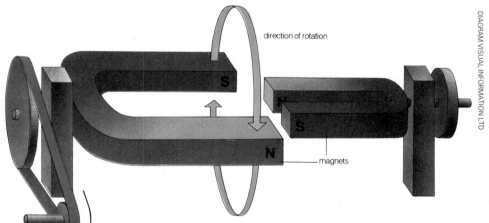

direction of rotation

magnets

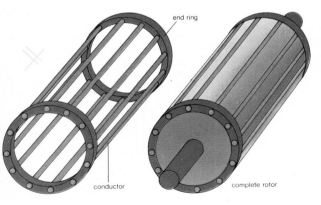

end ring

conductor

complete rotor

Above: a 'squirrel cage' (or nowadays, simply 'cage') induction motor has a rotor which consists of copper or aluminium bars joined at their ends by thick rings of the same material. The conductor alone is shown on the left with the complete rotor on the right. A rotating magnetic field generated in the stator induces currents in the cage which in turn produce a dragging force on the rotor and make it revolve.

Above: the principle of the synchronous motor. If the left hand horseshoe magnet is rotated in the direction shown, it will pull the right hand magnet around with it. If the right hand magnet has to do work, that is, if the shaft has to drive a load, it will rotate so that its poles are 'slightly behind' the primary poles. Only in this way can it develop force, but both magnets revolve at the same speed. In a commercial motor the two sets of magnet poles are arranged as concentric cylinders. The outer contains a number of coils carrying AC current which produce a rotating pole system (as in the induction motor) and the rotor is an electromagnet system fed with DC current.

repulsion motors (another form of single-phase AC commutator motor). Magnetic machines include reluctance and hysteresis motors, SOLENOIDS and RELAYS.

The classification into 'magnetic' and 'electromagnetic' machines is a comparatively recent concept and to some may seem artificial, since machines in both classes make use of electromagnets. But the difference between the two classes is of fundamental importance in appreciating the different uses to which motors of each class are put. Electromagnetic machines have a performance which improves naturally as they are made bigger. Magnetic machines, on the other hand, improve as they are scaled down to smaller sizes. The applications of reluctance and hysteresis motors are therefore restricted to such things as tape recorders, record players and electric clocks. Electromagnetic machines, in contrast, supply the needs of both heavy and light industry alike since they are quite effective down to the size of machine needed for washing machines and even hair dryers.

One unusual form of electric motor is the LINEAR INDUCTION MOTOR. This is little more than a rotary machine which has been split along a radial plane and 'unrolled' (with minor subsequent modifications). There are as many possible types of linear motor as there are rotary types listed above.

Induction motors When a magnet is moved across the face of an electrically conducting sheet it induces EDDY CURRENTS in the sheet and produces a force tending to drag the sheet

Below: this perspective view of a simple DC motor shows a single coil and pair of commutator segments. The 'field' magnets are on the outside—permanent magnets are used in small motors, electromagnets in larger machines. As the rotor (armature) coil rotates, the current through the coil is periodically reversed by the action of the commutator, thus maintaining the same direction of motive force.

Below: a reluctance motor as used in an electric clock. The teeth on the rotor try to line up with the stator teeth. They can do this permanently by staying motionless, as shown, but since the power supply is AC, an equally acceptable condition is where the speed of rotation is such that the two sets of teeth are directly opposite each other each time the magnetic field is at a maximum.

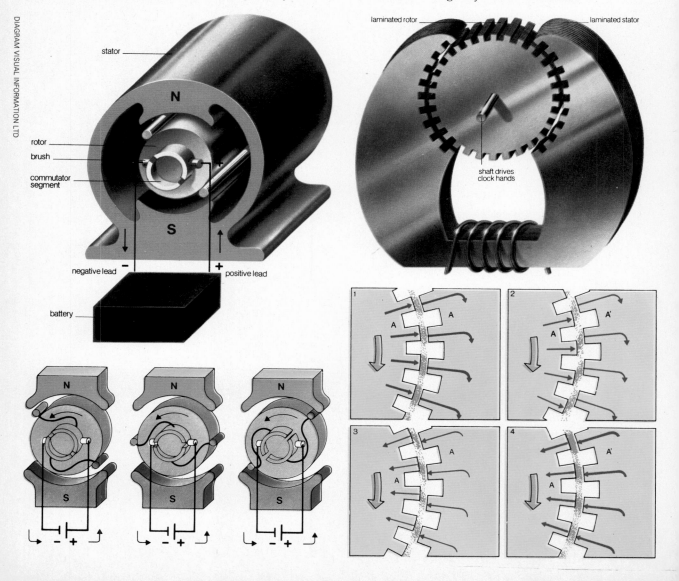

stator

rotor

brush

commutator segment

N

S

negative lead − + positive lead

battery

laminated rotor — laminated stator

shaft drives clock hands

N N N

S S S

− + − + − +

1 A A

2 A' A

3 A

4 A'

along with the magnet. This fact is less well known than the fact that a magnet will attract pieces of iron and steel, because the conducting sheet of the induction device can (and usually does) consist of copper or aluminium, which are classed as non-magnetic. This fact alone is an indication that magnetic things are very effective in small sizes, while induction devices (which are electromagnetic) are not very spectacular in small sizes. So while the principle of the induction motor cannot be illustrated by putting a small coin on a table and sweeping a magnet over it from side to side, such an arrangement does produce a very small force on the coin, and if the experiment were to be repeated with a copper disc 12 inches (30 cm) in diameter and a large magnet, a large force would be obtained.

Yet such a system cannot be described as a 'motor' because mechanical force (on the magnet) is needed to provide mechanical force on the sheet. It is, at best, a clutch. To make an induction motor, the moving magnet must be replaced by a system of fixed electromagnets which are fed with currents which change in such a way as to produce the same effect as if a permanent magnet system had moved.

For an explanation of how such a thing is possible, imagine a ring of electric lamp bulbs which are being switched on and off one at a time in sequence around the ring. If this is done fairly rapidly, the effect is as if a spot of light is travelling around the ring, yet it is obvious from the physical structure that nothing actually moves. Now suppose instead only lamp

Below: how a hysteresis motor works. The magnet, as it rotates, magnetizes the steel disc. Once magnetized, however, it is not so easily demagnetized and it tends to be dragged around with the magnet. Eventually, the disc travels at the same speed as the magnet, at which point the disc is said to be 'locked' to it. Any load on the disc will break the lock and reduce its speed.

Below: when a conductor is moved in a magnetic field a voltage is created, or induced, across it. If the ends of the conductor are connected to a voltmeter, this will give a reading when the conductor is moved. If in the place of the voltmeter a battery is connected, then a current flows through the conductor and it experiences a sideways force. This force is used to produce motion in a motor.

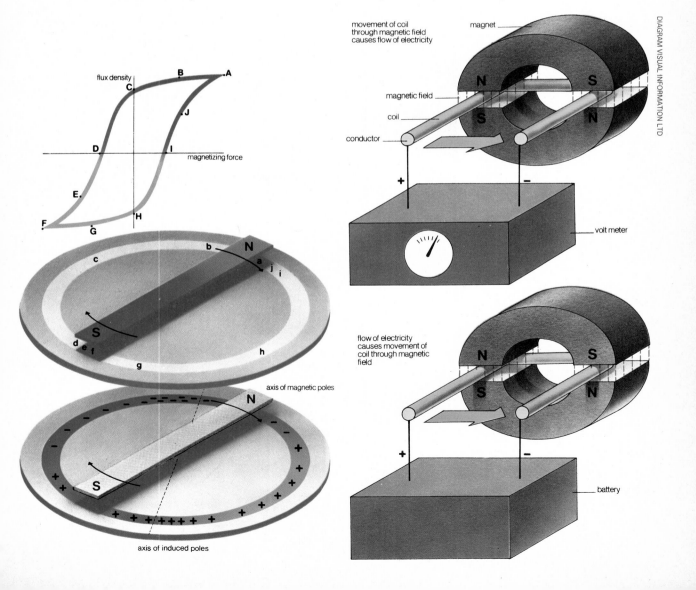

Below: a 60 hp induction motor. This is a four pole machine operating up to 1440 rpm with a power consumption of 45 kW and a current rating of 78.5 amps at 415 volts (three phase supply). It is built to metric standards, being 425 mm in diameter and 926 mm long.

Next to bottom: this reluctance motor is approximately seven inches in diameter and produces $\frac{1}{4}$ hp at a speed of 1425 rpm.

Bottom: a hysteresis motor. This is a compact motor, being only $4\frac{1}{2}$ inches in diameter, and has two operating speeds of 1000 and 3000 rpm. It is used as a capstan motor in computer tape decks.

numbers 1, 4, 7, 10 and so on, are switched on for a fraction of a second, then, as they are switched off, numbers 2, 5, 8, 11 are switched on, then 3, 6, 9, 12 and so on, a pattern of alternate light and dark patches will appear to rotate around the ring. The rotating magnetic field of the induction motor is produced in this way by arranging a ring of magnets on the stationary part of the machine. The magnets are energized in sequence and a pattern of north and south poles appears to travel around the periphery; this field is just as capable of inducing currents in a conducting cylinder as would be a system of permanent magnets which *actually* moved.

Instead of 'switching' the primary ring of electromagnets, they are simply fed from an AC supply which makes the whole machine cheap to build (for it has no commutator or brushes as in a DC motor) and very robust as the rotating member consists only of what is virtually a solid lump of metal. In most commercial machines the rotating member or 'rotor' is made up of a slotted steel core with copper or aluminium bars filling the slots and all connected together at each end of the rotor by a thick ring of the same material. In modern practice the bars and rings are usually cast into the slots at a single operation, a cooling fan often being incorporated at one end in the process of casting.

So desirable are the robust, reliable and low cost features of the induction motor, that over 90% of the world's horsepower of electric motors consists of induction machines.

Synchronous motors The production of induced current in an induction motor rotor depends on there being *relative* movement between the rotating field and the secondary

conductor. In other words, the rotor never quite 'catches up' with the field. If the rotor runs at 97% of the field speed, the 3% relative motion is referred to as the percentage *slip*. It is fairly obvious that the slip will increase with added load and for some applications such inability to maintain an exact speed is inadmissible. In such circumstances a motor is used whose rotor consists of an arrangement of permanent magnets or of DC-fed electromagnets. The primary coils are, exactly as in the case of the induction motor, arranged to produce a rotating magnetic field, but this time the field 'locks' with the field of the magnetized rotor. Thus the rotor speed cannot change with variation in load and it is said to run 'in synchronism' with the mains supply.

If the system of primary coils is so arranged as to give the impression that one pair of poles, that is, a 2-pole pattern (one north pole and one south pole) are contained in the full 360°, the field will rotate one revolution in one complete cycle of the AC mains supply. In Europe the supply frequency is usually 50 cycles per second (denoted '50 hertz'). In America the standard frequency is 60 hertz. Thus a 2-pole motor on 50 Hz supply has a field speed of 50 revolutions per second or 3000 revolutions per minute (rpm). If the primary coils are arranged

Below left: the motor room of the platemill at the Motherwell Works of the Scottish Shelton and East Moors Group of the British Steel Corporation. This shows two 3430 kW, 1120 volts DC main mill motors with two operating speeds of 40 and 80 rpm.

Below right: a cutaway of a 3-phase squirrel cage rotor induction motor.

to give a 4-pole pattern, the speed is halved, and so on, so the possible synchronous motor speeds in Europe are 3000, 1500, 1000, 750, 600, 500 and so on, rpm. Corresponding induction motor speeds are less than these values by the small amount of slip necessary to induce secondary current. A disadvantage of the synchronous motor is that it cannot self-start and the speed must be brought to within a very small percentage of synchronism before magnetic 'locking' can take place. The synchronous machine is more commonly used as a generator or ALTERNATOR, almost all the power stations in Britain employing machines of this type.

DC and AC commutator motors   There are two dis-advantages common to both induction motors and synchronous motors. Neither is able to provide efficient speed variation over a wide range without a variable supply frequency. Neither is able to provide speeds over 3000 rpm when fed directly from mains supply. Where high speed or variable speed electric drive is required for use from mains supply, a commutator motor is used. The action of a commutator is fairly complicated and more easily explained for the case of DC machines.

In a DC machine the stationary part (stator) consists of a ring of DC-fed 'field' magnets. The rotor is, like the induction motor, a series of conducting wires or bars in slots in a steel core. In this case, however, they are insulated coils rather than solid cast bars (and therefore more expensive to make) and each coil has its ends connected to a pair of conducting segments mounted on an insulating block on the rotor shaft at one end of the rotor. Connection to the rotor coils is made by carbon blocks or copper gauze 'brushes' which make contact

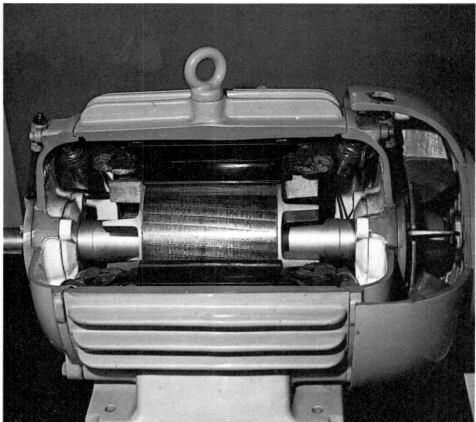

with pairs of commutator segments twice per cycle. In this way current flowing in the appropriate direction can be fed to the rotor coils only when they are opposite the appropriate field pole (north or south). The 'appropriate direction' means that for all coils the force produced will be in the same direction at all speeds and loads for the ring of segments and the brushes provide automatic switching to ensure that this is so.

The disadvantage of commutator motors are that sparking tends to occur between commutator segments and brushes, which eats away the metal of the segment. Even without sparks the rubbing of brush on segments wears away both and more maintenance is required than in the case of brushless machines. Power electronics have tended to increase the popularity of the DC machine, although the small single phase AC commutator motor (generally known as a universal motor since it can also run on DC) is still the principal form of drive for household devices requiring high speed, such as vacuum cleaners and 'do-it-yourself' power drills.

Reluctance motors   A reluctance motor is simply a synchronous motor with the magnetized rotor replaced by an unmagnetized piece of steel so shaped that it has a number of 'preferred' positions into which it will settle for any given primary field configuration. A preferred position is one in which the 'resistance' of the magnetic circuit (which is called *reluctance*) is a minimum, hence the name of this type of motor. The induction motor is 'king' so far as total power of electric drives is concerned, but there are probably more reluctance

motors in terms of *numbers* only, for the reluctance motor is the drive from mains-fed electric clocks, their synchronous running being frequency-dependent only. Since the main electricity supply is controlled to keep in step with Standard Time, all mains-fed clocks must indicate the same readings relative to each other. Auxiliary starting mechanisms are, of course, needed for clock motors.

Hysteresis motor   A hysteresis motor is even simpler in construction than a clock motor for the rotor can be a smooth cylinder. The steel used to make the rotor is, however, very similar to that used to make permanent magnets (unlike that of all other types of motor), so that as the moving magnetic field passes over any point on the rotor (in induction motor language we should say 'slips') it leaves the part passed over permanently magnetized. This 'hysteretic lag' produces force and tends to make the motor run more and more nearly as a synchronous motor as it speeds up, until finally it suceeds in locking in on the rotating field. Unlike the reluctance motor, however, it is capable of driving loads at all speeds up to synchronism, but of course, synchronism is never guaranteed, as in the reluctance machine.

Below left: a linear induction motor is like a rotary motor rolled out into a straight line. This picture shows the field winding arrangement.

Below: a study of the magnetic field pattern of a linear induction motor. A moving field will produce a force on metallic objects nearby.

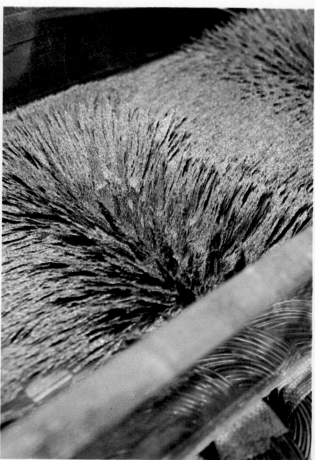

ELECTRIC VEHICLES

Electric vehicles are often thought of as a new development, but as long ago as 1837 Robert Davidson of Aberdeen built an electric carriage powered by a crude iron-zinc BATTERY and driven by a very simple ELECTRIC MOTOR, which contained all the basic elements of the modern electric vehicle.

The advent of the lead-acid battery allowed the first commercial battery operated vehicle to be introduced in 1881 by the Paris Omnibus Company. London had its first electric bus in 1888, and also the world's first mechanically propelled taxicabs which were built by W C Bersey in 1897 for the London Electric Cab Co Ltd, and operated for two years.

Around the turn of the century the first land speed record was set in France by a battery driven car. In 1898 the flying kilometre was completed at an average speed of 63 km/h (39 mile/h), and in 1899 this was raised to 106 km/h (66 mile/h), by the Belgian, Camille Jenatzy, in his bullet-shaped electric car called 'La Jamais Contente'. By 1902 technical improvements enabled Charles Baker, an American, to attain over 85 mile/h (137 km/h), but unfortunately on his third and officially timed run the car suffered a mechanical failure and so no official world record was obtained. The most recent speed record for an electric car was attained by the 'Silver Eagle' developed by Eagle Picher Industries in the USA. In August

Below: Camille Jenatzy of Belgium with his record-breaking electric car 'La Jamais Contente', in which he raised the world land speed record to 106 km/h (66 mile/h) in 1899 at Acheres, France.

1971, at Bonneville, the car completed the flying kilometre at an average speed of 152.59 mile/h (about 245 km/h) and covered a mile from a standing start at an average of 146.437 mile/h (about 236 km/h).

By the early 1900s a high proportion of the cars on the roads of London, New York and Paris were battery electric, and electric cars became very fashionable. The rapid development of the INTERNAL COMBUSTION ENGINE, however, accelerated still faster by World War 1, meant that by the 1920s electric cars could no longer compete in terms of speed, acceleration and range. Between the wars many electric car companies came and went. One of the best known English makes was the Partridge Wilson 'Brougham' of 1936, powered by a 60 volt 324 ampere hour battery which gave it a claimed maximum speed of 32 mile/h (51.5 km/h) and a range of 60 miles (97 km) per charge. This was typical for most electric cars of that time, and would be considered insufficient for most purposes by the average user today.

The factors which lead the private buyer to reject the electric car did not affect the commercial user in the same way. Electric vans and trucks were developed in parallel with the cars, and today in Britain for example there are some 55,000 electric vehicles in use performing a variety of tasks such as local authority duties, milk delivery and postal work, all of which involve a significant amount of stop-start driving. The electric milk truck is ideally suited for this arduous stop-start kind of work, and whereas the DIESEL powered version lasts only 3 to 5 years the electric one has a useful life of over twenty years.

position of handbrake

steering wheel

bumper

suspension unit

OSBORNE/MARKS

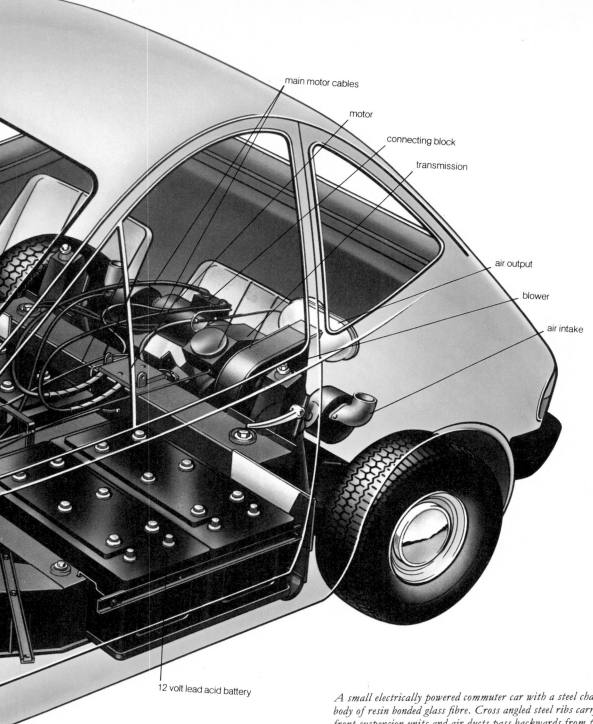

main motor cables

motor

connecting block

transmission

air output

blower

air intake

12 volt lead acid battery

A small electrically powered commuter car with a steel chassis and a body of resin bonded glass fibre. Cross angled steel ribs carry the front suspension units and air ducts pass backwards from the front of the car for heating and ventilation. Situated underneath the plastic seats are four standard 12 volt lead acid batteries which supply power to two electric motors each of 5 bhp maximum. These are air cooled and the hot air can be recirculated for interior heating. Only brake and accelerator pedals are necessary, as the control characteristics of the electric motors obviate the need for clutch and gearbox. Spent batteries can be recharged from the mains, using a transformer, or replaced with a fresh, fully charged set.

Electrically powered FORK LIFT TRUCKS are in common use the world over. (See also TRAM [streetcar] and TROLLEY BUS.)

Basic design   The electric vehicle is basically a very simple machine; it can be said to have only five basic components and eight moving parts, four of which are wheels. In essence it consists of the battery, a controller, the motor, the transmission, and the vehicle chassis and body, and it was for this reason that so much interest was shown in it in the early days of powered transport. Apart from the battery, controller and motor, the design of electric vehicles usually follows conventional lines.

Most batteries in use today are of the lead-acid type. Originally based on the flat plate design, modern traction cells are now of tubular construction. This type of battery, provided it is regularly charged and the electrolyte level is maintained, has a guaranteed life of four years, which is regularly exceeded in practice. It is, however, rather heavy and the *energy density* (the amount of energy produced per unit weight) is only about 11 watt-hours per lb (approximately 24Wh/kg), and this is the feature principally responsible for the poor road performance of most electric vehicles. Where vehicles are used comparatively infrequently, as in mining and tunnelling, nickel-iron batteries are often used as they can stand long periods of non-use without attention.

Speed control   The motor in most electric road vehicles is a low speed DC series wound type driving the rear wheels through a conventional back axle arrangement. Speed control is carried out in two main ways. The simplest is to change the voltage applied to the motor by tapping the battery in a combination of series-parallel connections. For example, if a 48 volt battery is used it is initially connected for 12 V to limit the high current needed for starting, and once the vehicle is on the move the controller switches the connections to give 24 V, then 36 V and ultimately the full 48 V. Most electric vehicles are controlled via a conventional type of accelerator pedal, the only other foot pedal being that for the brake. As the only controls needed in electric vehicles are the accelerator, brakes, and steering they are particularly easy to drive.

A more advanced form of control of the motor speed can be provided by the use of THYRISTORS, which are solid state 'switches' that allow the current to be supplied in bursts. For starting and acceleration the thyristor conducts for short periods limiting the energy supplied. As the speed increases the length of the thyristors' conducting periods are increased so that maximum power can be developed.

Commercial vehicles   Considerable interest has been shown recently in electric road vehicles, because the high levels of noise and pollution so common with petrol [gasoline] and diesel engines are absent. In terms of resources, the electric vehicle also competes on equal terms, being no less efficient and frequently more efficient in overall energy consumption than its internal combustion counterpart.

Extensive research programmes are under way in many parts of the world to produce designs which will provide road performances comparable to conventional vehicles. The major difficulty with the electric vehicle has been to find a battery which will give sufficient energy from a realistic weight. The standard lead-acid traction cell is really too heavy, although the most recent designs will now give 16 to 18 watt-hours per lb (35 to 39 Wh/kg) and working lives of up to 800 charging cycles are predicted. Using this type of battery, Chloride/Selnec in Britain and RWE/Varta/MAN in Germany have produced buses capable of carrying 50 passengers and operating conventional services, both types being capable of about

GES. GERMANY

Top left: the Enfield 8000 electric car, a two seater designed primarily for use in urban areas. It has a range of 40 to 50 miles (64 to 80 km).

Top right: the batteries for the MAN electric bus are carried on a trailer, so they do not take up any space in the bus itself. When the batteries are run down they are exchanged for a charged set, as shown here.

Left: the chassis layout of the Ford 'Comuta' electric town car. The front chassis section carries the steering, pedals, front shock absorbers and ducts for the heating and ventilation system. The batteries are on the centre section, and the two electric motors are at the rear.

Below: a lightweight electric powered motorcycle.

HART ASSOCIATES

45 mile/h (72 km/h) with a range of about 40 miles (64 km). To prevent the vehicles having to stand idle for lengthy periods while their batteries are recharged, they are designed so that the run-down batteries can be quickly exchanged for a fully charged set. The MAN bus carries its batteries in a trailer, and in the Chloride bus they are under the floor.

Many light electric vans are now being developed. In Germany a conversion of the standard Volkswagen van is so designed that the battery can be rapidly charged, and in Britain the Electricity Council and J Lucas Ltd have produced modified versions of British Leyland and Bedford vans. The former uses a mechanical gearbox and a high speed motor and the latter a variable speed motor controlled by thyristors. Both are capable of up to 50 mile/h (80 km/h). In the USA the Electric Vehicle Council have ordered a large number of vans from Battronic for use by electricity utilities throughout the country. Similar schemes are being undertaken in many other countries; Japan in particular is investing heavily in research.

The van is a particularly useful test vehicle in that the extra space available compared with a car allows new energy sources to be tested easily. In the USA for example General Motors have produced a FUEL CELL powered van with liquid hydrogen and oxygen being carried in cryogenic (low temperature) tanks. In Britain the Electricity Council has used one of its van conversions to demonstrate the first sodium-sulphur battery, which gave an energy density of 30 Wh/lb (66 Wh/kg). Later developments are expected to give as much as 154 Wh/lb (31.5 Wh/kg). Many other types of battery are also being tested such as the zinc-chlorine (Udylite, USA) and the zinc-air (Sony, Japan).

Electric cars The electric vehicle development which creates most public interest is the battery car. To date no really successful product has been sold, and early visions of cheap electric town cars are receding. The majority of cars so far produced have been conversions of existing products, and although the major car manufacturers have produced or sponsored prototype designs they have as yet made no really significant contribution. In France, Electricité de France have produced conversions of the Renault R4 (reducing it to a two seater in the process) and in Italy ENEL have converted a Fiat. In the USA there have been successful conversions of large-bodied cars which have speeds of up to 60 mile/h (97 km/h) and ranges of up to 100 miles (161 km), but no large scale production has been started.

The electric car as a product presents several design problems. It is becoming more difficult to design small cars which will comply with new safety regulations, and the extra mass of batteries in the electric car present additional difficulties. The majority of purpose built cars have so far been lightly constructed vehicles unlikely to pass stringent tests. The Enfield 8000, which has been ordered by the Electricity Council in England, has overcome these problems. This two seater, which is designed to have a low aerodynamic drag and rolling resistance, is powered by electric batteries and has a top speed of over 40 mile/h (64 km/h), rapid acceleration and a range under normal conditions of 40 to 50 miles (64 to 80 km). This performance allows it to operate well in normal traffic, making it an attractive town car.

A recent development is the introduction of lightweight electric motorcycles, such as that produced by the Austrian firm of Steyr-Daimler-Puch, which may prove to be a useful form of personal transport in busy city centres.

ELECTROCARDIOGRAPH (see electronics in medicine)

ELECTROCHEMICAL MACHINING

In conventional mechanical machining, metals are shaped by cutting 'chips' of material (called swarf) off the workpiece surface, using a sharp-edged tool. Of course the cutting edge should be harder than the surface being machined, and this means that there are problems in machining very hard materials. The tools can wear and there is a lower limit to the amount of metal which can be removed by a single cut. Below this limit the tool will simply skid across the surface. Additionally, troubles can arise due to stresses induced in machined surfaces and the formation of 'rags' or 'burrs' where metal squeezes over edges.

Electrochemical machining offers a way of overcoming these drawbacks. This is because metal is removed from the workpiece by an electrolytic rather than a mechanical process. The workpiece is made the anode (the positive electrode) and is immersed in a suitable electrolyte (see ELECTROLYSIS).

The negative electrode, the cathode, which is also immersed in the electrolyte, in this case acts as the 'tool', or more correctly as a die because it is shaped according to the form of the finished surface which is desired. It is held very close to the anode at distances of about 1 mm (several hundredths of an inch). This reduces power loss when high currents are passed and ensures that current does not spread out but is confined to that part of the surface which it is intended to 'machine'. Part of the cathode may be shielded with an insulator to achieve the same purpose.

When the electric current flows, the metal atoms at the anode's surface lose electrons and become transformed into positively charged metal ions which dissolve in the electrolyte. Thus atoms are removed and the surface recedes.

In some applications, electrochemical machining is used for shaping articles which must be finished to precise dimensions. The amount of metal removed from the surface depends on the quantity of electric current that is passed, according to Faraday's Laws, thus the depth of the 'cut' can be accurately controlled.

The main reason for the use of electrochemical methods is, however, excessive hardness of the metal to be treated. Usually very simple electrolytes are used, such as solutions of common salt, sodium chloride. The electrolyte is pumped in between the anode and cathode at high speed so as to rapidly remove the dissolved metal. This is important since otherwise a sludge can form which will prevent uniform machining. As it is, the sludge forms subsequently and is removed by filtering before the electrolyte is recirculated.

In order to remove metal at a useful rate, very high currents have to be passed through the anode surface, perhaps up to 5000 amps per square decimetre (about 50,000 amps per sq ft). This limits the size of a surface that can be machined at any one time, since equipment to produce very high direct currents becomes very expensive and cumbersome. Considerable heat can also be developed by these high currents so that a cooling device is often included in the system. A typical application of

An electrochemical deburring machine removes burrs from automatically machined components. While the operator loads one compartment, the tool can be seen descending over the load in the other side. When it is positioned, the electrolyte flows and current is passed.

electrochemical machining is the shaping of the blades of gas turbine engines, which are made of very hard oxidation-resistant nickel-base alloys.

Sometimes machining is combined with a smoothing or polishing action. Mixtures of strong acids are used for electrolytes and the currents applied are about 50 amps per square decimetre (500 amps per sq ft). Gear wheels, for example, might be treated so as to remove the burrs left by mechanical machining. Another example is the finishing of the stainless steel drums of automatic washing machines. Electrochemical treatment gives a pleasing bright appearance, as well as removing tiny ragged edges which might snag clothing.

Spark machining Spark machining, or electrospark machining, is similar to electrochemical machining except that a dielectric (non-conductor) instead of an electrolyte is used, which does not pass current until a high voltage is reached. At this point a spark discharge occurs between the electrodes and metal is removed from the workpiece. This method achieves a higher rate of metal removal and greater dimensional precision, and is used in the machining of cavity dies.

ELECTROENCEPHALOGRAPH (see electronics in medicine)

Below: diagram illustrating the process of electrochemical machining. An electric current is passed between a closely fitting die, which forms the cathode, and the anode, which is the workpiece. Metal from the surface being machined passes into solution in the electrolyte, which flows between the two electrodes at a rate fast enough to carry away the metallic ions and prevent any deposition on the cathode.

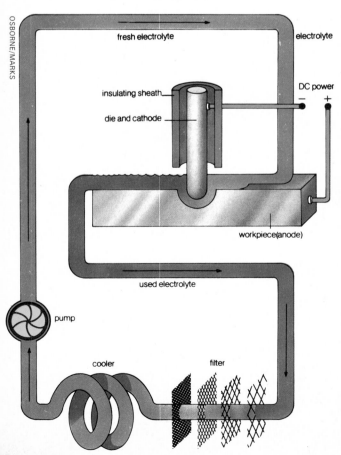

fresh electrolyte

electrolyte

insulating sheath

die and cathode

DC power

− +

workpiece (anode)

used electrolyte

pump

cooler

filter

ELECTROLYSIS

Electrolysis is the chemical conversion or breakup of a compound by passing an electric current through the compound, which must be in a fluid state, either dissolved as a solution or molten. Although the phenomenon was discovered within months of the invention of the electric battery by VOLTA in the year 1800, it was Michael FARADAY (1791–1867) who, some two decades later, was able to formulate the laws of electrolysis.

The electrically conducting fluid through which the current passes is known as the *electrolyte* and contains electrically charged particles called IONS (from the Greek word for 'going'). For example when common salt, sodium chloride, NaCl, is dissolved in water it splits up into positively charged *cations* of sodium, Na^+, and negatively charged *anions* of chlorine, Cl^-. It is these ions that carry the current, whereas in metals the current is carried by the electrons. When an electric current is passed through the electrolyte by means of electrodes which are immersed in it, the anions are attracted to the positively charged anode and the cations are attracted to the negative cathode, the opposite charges attracting one another. It is this movement of charged ions which produces a flow of electric current, but it is at the electrodes, where a transfer of current takes place, that the reactions of electrolysis occur. Thus substances which do not release ions cannot conduct electricity in this manner and cannot be electrolyzed.

The conducting wires leading to the electrodes will be metallic, and they conduct electricity by the movement of electrons along them. Each electron bears a single unit negative charge and the current in amperes is really a measure of how many electrons pass any point in the circuit in a given time. At a cathode, electrons flow down into the electrode and they then react with cations, causing a chemical change to them. Hydrogen ions, H^+, for example, are converted into hydrogen atoms, H, after taking up one electron. Subsequently the atoms form molecules of hydrogen gas (H_2) which bubbles off. At an anode, electrons are given up by the anions and pass away through the connecting wire, thereby altering the chemical nature of the ions. Alternatively the atoms of the electrode itself could give up electrons and dissolve in the electrolyte as cations. This is the basis of metallic corrosion.

Since the ions each have a fixed weight and electrical charge and therefore react with a fixed number of electrons it is easy to see the basis of Faraday's Laws of Electrolysis, which state that the weight of substance changed by electrolysis is proportional to its equivalent weight (the weight of a fixed number of ions divided by the electrical charge of each one) and also to the current that has passed and the duration of electrolysis. Because of the validity of these laws, electrolysis may be used as a method of chemical analysis since the quantity of a substance present may be measured by the amount of electricity required to electrolyze it. In practice unwanted 'side reactions' may occur and consume some of the current intended for the main electrolytic reaction. The electrolysis is then described as operating at reduced efficiency, say 75% or 60%, although Faraday's Laws are in fact being obeyed.

It is possible to reverse the process of electrolysis so that chemicals are made to react on an electrode surface and produce electric current as they do so. Such an arrangement is used in the construction of a FUEL CELL.

Chemical production The electrolysis of sodium chloride was one of the earliest large scale applications of electrochemistry to industrial production and it provides a good example of how technical problems are overcome in

practice. When common salt is dissolved in water it splits up into ions. If the brine is electrolyzed in a very simple *cell* (arrangement of anode, cathode and electrolyte) using inert metal electrodes, the chlorine ions, Cl^-, travel to the anode, release their electrons and are discharged as chlorine gas. This is a valuable raw material for producing such substances as solvents, bleach and plastics. At the cathode, however, the electrical forces are unable to discharge the sodium ions, Na^+. This is because water molecules have a greater affinity for electrons than do sodium ions. The water, H_2O, takes up one electron and splits up to give atoms of hydrogen, H, which combine to give molecules of hydrogen gas, H_2, leaving hydroxyl anions, OH^-, in the solution. Thus the solution builds up an effective concentration of sodium hydroxide or caustic soda, NaOH. This is itself another valuable product, but in the simple cell it is difficult to separate since it is mixed with the original sodium chloride. The alkaline solution formed can also give off oxygen at the anode, which is an undesirable side reaction.

Above left: apparatus used by Sir Humphry Davy for his electrolysis experiments early in the 1800s. He discovered sodium by passing a strong electric current from a battery through fused sodium hydroxide.

Left: electrolytic cells for the refining of silver. The impure silver is made the anode, pure silver depositing on the cathode.

Below left: a vast cell room for the electrolysis of brine to obtain chlorine gas with sodium hydroxide as a by-product. Plant engineers are standing on top of the cells. The brine is pumped from brine 'fields' where it is made by mixing water with salt deposits.

Right: a diagram representing the commercial electrolysis of brine with a split cell. It is electrolyzed using an inert anode and mercury cathode. At the anode chlorine is evolved, while at the cathode sodium ions receive an electron becoming sodium metal. This dissolves in the mercury forming an amalgam which is passed to the next compartment. Here the sodium re-ionizes and dissolves in the electrolyte. At the cathode hydrogen is evolved and hydroxyl ions form, thus giving a solution of sodium hydroxide.

Far right: the simple electrolysis of brine. The chlorine ions are attracted to the anode where they release their electrons and are discharged as chlorine gas. The sodium ions move towards the cathode where they are in competition for electrons with the water molecules. But water molecules have a greater affinity for electrons and take up one each splitting into hydrogen atoms and leaving hydroxyl ions behind.

These difficulties were overcome by the use of a cell of split design in which there were separate anode and cathode compartments. In the Castner-Kellner cell sodium chloride is electrolyzed using an inert anode and a mercury cathode. At the anode, chlorine is evolved and at the cathode sodium ions are discharged to give sodium metal. This is possible because it is difficult for hydrogen to form on a mercury surface, but sodium atoms are dissolved in the mercury to form a liquid amalgam. This amalgam is transferred to the second compartment of the cell by a rocking movement or by pumping and here the mercury acts as an anode. The sodium re-ionizes and dissolves in the electrolyte. At the cathode hydrogen is evolved and hydroxyl ions form, so giving a solution of sodium hydroxide.

Metal refining
Electrolytic processes are also important for the production of pure metals.

At one time the only method of producing aluminium was by a very expensive chemical process. The metal was much too costly for general use and was considered a rare and precious material, being used by Napoleon III for dinner services and military uniforms. The present abundance of cheap aluminium is due entirely to the development of an electrolytic process.

The details of aluminium refining have already been described (see ALUMINIUM EXTRACTION) and several other reactive metals are extracted in a similar manner. These metals are like sodium in that they cannot easily be produced by electrolysis of solutions of their salts in water. All that happens at the cathode is the production of hydrogen from the water. This problem is overcome by dissolving the salts in molten salt baths where water is absent. In the extraction of magnesium, for example, the chloride salt is dissolved in a hot molten

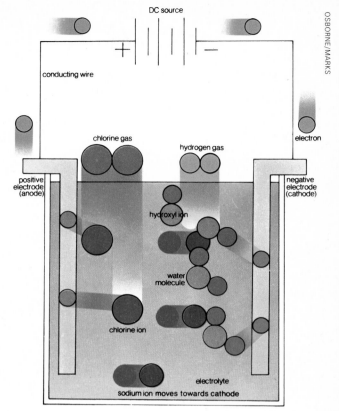

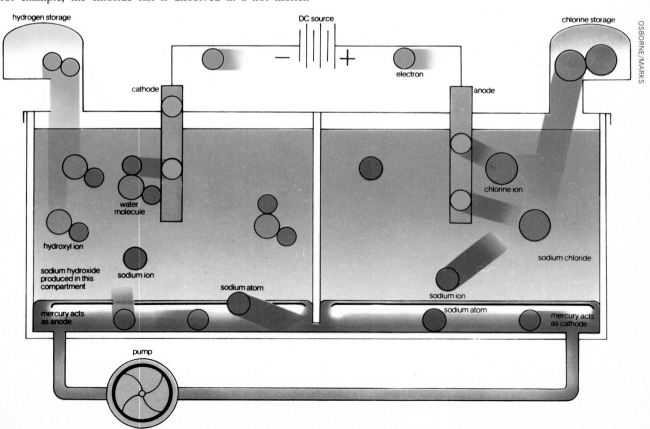

mixture of sodium and calcium chlorides. The magnesium chloride splits up to give Mg^{2+} cations and twice as many Cl^- anions. After electrolysis the chlorine produced at the anode is piped away and the molten magnesium metal is of such low density that it floats as a pool on top of the molten salt, being easily ladled off periodically.

COPPER is purified by electrolysis but in this case the process is much simpler since copper ions, Cu^{2+}, will easily take up electrons and deposit as metal on a cathode, even in aqueous solutions. An electrolyte of sulphuric acid and copper sulphate is used and the impure copper is made the anode. Here it dissolves, releasing Cu^{2+} ions into the electrolyte. Impurities, which may include useful quantities of precious metals, do not dissolve and fall to the bottom as a sludge. The copper deposits on the cathode at about 99.98% purity.

Power generation   It has been suggested that electrolysis could provide a basis for storing and distributing solar energy. The electricity derived from power obtained from the sun could be used to electrolyze water, splitting it up into oxygen and hydrogen. The hydrogen could be used as a fuel for domestic and industrial use and even perhaps for motor vehicles. It could be fairly easily stored, and would cause no pollution when burnt since the only product of combustion would be water.

ELECTROLYTE (see electrolysis)

Below : electrolysis is also used for the removal of unwanted hair. One electrode makes a relatively large contact with the skin, while the second one is needle-shaped and is applied to the hair root. When a current is passed, at the small electrode it concentrates on a small area and the chemical changes produced kill the hair root.

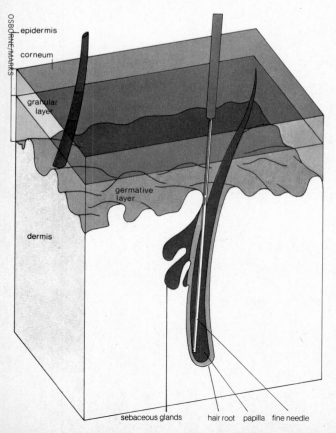

epidermis
corneum
granular layer
germative layer
dermis
sebaceous glands   hair root   papilla   fine needle

OSBORNE/MARKS

ELECTROMAGNETIC RADIATION

Many apparently unrelated phenomena, such as light, radio waves and X-rays are different examples of just one type of radiation, *electromagnetic* radiation. They are in fact waves of ENERGY produced when an electric charge is accelerated.

A stationary electric charge—in practice, a charged particle such as an ELECTRON—is surrounded by *lines of force* which indicate the direction in which another similar charge would move if it were placed near the original charge. If the charge is moved up and down it is decelerated and then accelerated in the opposite direction at each end of the path. These accelerations cause 'kinks' in the lines of force, which move outwards from the charge. A moving charge, however, also generates a magnetic field. (This is the principle of ELECTROMAGNETISM, in which the current of moving electrons produces a controllable magnetic field). An accelerating charge generates a 'kinked' magnetic field, whose lines of force are perpendicular to the electric field. The speed at which these 'kinks' move outwards depends on what kind of material is surrounding the charge, but in a vacuum it is 299,792.456 km per second (186,282 miles per second).

James Clerk MAXWELL was the first to calculate that these 'electromagnetic' disturbances could exist, and would travel at this velocity. He noticed that this is the same as the measured speed of light, and suggested that light is a form of electromagnetic radiation. At the time it seemed necessary that these 'waves' should be vibrating in some mysterious medium, which was called the aether or ETHER. This had the curious properties that it filled all of space, was far more rigid than steel, yet could not be detected except by the vibrations in it. EINSTEIN's Special Theory of RELATIVITY, however, showed that electromagnetic waves can travel without any medium to support them, and so the ether is no longer believed in.

Frequency and wavelength   To produce a continuous wave of electromagnetic radiation, the charge must be vibrated up and down continuously. The number of vibrations of the charge in one second is called the *frequency* of the resulting wave, and is measured in cycles per second or *Hertz* (Hz), after the scientist who first produced and detected radio waves. The lowest frequencies of interest are around 150,000 Hz (150 kHz), which are 'long wave' radio frequencies. VHF radio uses radiation at about 100,000,000 Hz (100 MHz), while light is at very much higher frequencies (600,000 GHz) and X-rays higher still (3,000,000,000 GHz).

Another way of distinguishing types of electromagnetic radiation is by its wavelength, the distance between successive 'crests' of the wave. For any type of wave it must be true that velocity of wave = frequency × wavelength.

It was mentioned above that electromagnetic radiation travels at different speeds in different materials, and so the wavelength must also vary according to the medium the wave is passing through—the frequency is always constant. The 'wavelength' of a particular radiation usually means the wavelength it would have in a vacuum. For example, the yellow light emitted by a sodium lamp has a wavelength of 589.3 nanometres in a vacuum. (1 nanometre is one thousand millionth of a metre, and is abbreviated to nm. Wavelengths can also be given in angstroms, where 589.3 nm = 5893 A). In air it is reduced to 589.1 nm, and in glass it is only 388.6 nm.

The longest radio waves are more than 10,000 m (over 6 miles), while the shortest waves (gamma rays) are at wavelengths less than 0.001 nm, smaller than an atom. (Note that low frequencies correspond to long wavelengths, and high

frequencies to short wavelengths).

Radio waves Electromagnetic waves longer than 1 mm are known as radio waves. They are subdivided into groups, such as very high frequency (VHF) and ultra high frequency (UHF), depending on their frequency. The very longest waves usually detectable are called VLF, for very low frequency, with wavelengths longer than 10 km and frequencies lower than 30,000 Hz. At this end of the scale, it becomes rather impractical to detect the signals, which are of very low energy.

Radio transmitters work on the principle of rapidly switching on and off an electric current. Whenever current is switched on, as in, for example, some domestic appliance, one pulse of electromagnetic radiation—one 'kink' in the lines of force—is produced. If the current is switched on and off at a high frequency, then electromagnetic radiation of that frequency will be produced. This is how radio transmitters work in principle: electrons are forced to pulsate at the chosen frequency along the transmitting AERIAL [antenna], which should for greatest efficiency be as long as the wavelength being emitted.

The electrons which constitute the current are accelerated as the current changes, and they radiate electromagnetic waves whose electric field is parallel to the transmitting aerial. If this aerial is vertical, only a vertical aerial will receive the radiation; it is said to be vertically *polarized*. Similarly a horizontal aerial will radiate horizontally polarized radiation, which can be detected only by a horizontal receiving aerial. (POLARIZATION can be produced in all forms of electromagnetic radiation, and has useful properties.) The electromagnetic wave produces currents in the receiving aerial which are amplified in the receiver to reproduce the transmitted message.

The highest frequency that can be produced electronically is about 300,000,000,000 Hz, corresponding to a wavelength

Top: the basis of TV and microwave transmitters is not so much the aerial as the electronic device which produces the electron pulses. This is a klystron, which produces pulses in a beam of electrons flowing along the horizontal tube, creating high frequency radiation.

Above: this diplexer unit in a TV station mixes sound and vision UHF signals of high power, just before they are fed to the aerial.

Below left: the Sun is a vast source of electromagnetic radiation of almost all wavelengths, but its peak is in the yellow part of the spectrum, characteristic of a body at about 6000°C. Some stars are much hotter, and appear blue; others have surface temperatures as low as 3000°C, cooler than a light bulb, though their size produces a vast output. The link between colour and temperature is shown at right: the hottest parts of this test model in a wind tunnel glow almost blue.

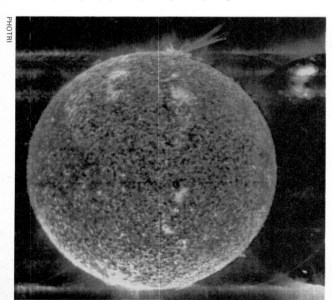

of 1 mm. Since the term 'radio' usually refers to electronically produced radiation this marks the end of the radio region.

Higher frequencies can be reached by using the natural vibrations of the molecules in a solid. These molecules contain electrons which generate electromagnetic radiation as the molecules vibrate. The hotter the solid is, the more rapidly the molecules vibrate, and the higher the frequency of the radiated electromagnetic waves. Radiation produced in this way is normally unpolarized, because polarization due to electrons moving in different directions will tend to cancel out.

Black body radiation Not all the radiation is at the same wavelength, however, even for an object at a constant temperature, and the way in which the energy of the emitted waves changes with frequency is shown in the diagram for bodies at different temperatures. This is a calculated curve, based on the behaviour of a theoretical 'black body', which absorbs all the radiation falling on it, and emits it at different wavelengths, but all substances behave something like this if they are placed inside a closed oven. A body as hot as the Sun radiates most energy at wavelengths around 520 nm, which is the wavelength of yellow-green light: while an object at room temperature emits far less radiation, most of it about 10,000 nm, beyond the visible spectrum, in the infra-red.

The infra-red lies between visible light and the radio region of the electromagnetic spectrum. The radio wavelengths shorter than 1 m are known as *microwaves*, and they share some properties with infra-red. The boundary with the latter occurs at about 1 mm, but the distinction usually made is that radio waves are generated electronically, while infra-red is produced thermally.

Infra-red is often thought of as 'heat radiation'. The reason for this is not because it has more energy than other wavelengths; the Sun, for example, radiates much more energy as visible light than as infra-red. It is because the molecules in objects at room temperature vibrate at about the same frequency as infra-red, so the radiation can give up its energy directly to the vibrating molecules. This extra energy makes the molecules vibrate faster, which is felt as heat. Yellow light from the Sun, however, will heat up an object much more than infra-red will.

Infra-red radiation cannot be detected by the type of receiver used for radio waves, but it can be measured with a BOLOMETER, which measures the total intensity of radiation received, and by some types of electronic detector.

Light Visible light is at shorter wavelengths than infra-red, from 390 to 750 nm. The eye sees different wavelengths as different colours: 680 nm is seen as red; 560 nm, yellow; 500 nm, green; 420 nm, blue; 400 nm, violet. The usual sources of light are hot bodies, such as the Sun or the filament of a tungsten lamp, and light is usually detected either by the eye, by the photographic plate, or by a PHOTOELECTRIC CELL.

To understand why these respond to light but not to infra-red radiation, it must be realized that electromagnetic radiation does not travel as a continuous flow of energy, but in bursts of energy, called quanta (or photons). The energy of each QUANTUM depends only on the frequency of the radiation:
Energy (in joules) $= 66 \times 10^{-38} \times$ frequency (in Hz).
For comparison, a 100 watt light bulb emits 100 joules of energy every second. The important thing to notice is that higher frequencies have photons of higher energy.

At the frequency of visible light the energy of a photon is only 4×10^{-19} joules, but this is enough to start some chemical reactions. In the eye the reaction triggers a nerve cell which transmits a message to the brain, while in the photographic FILM emulsion some of the silver compound is changed to

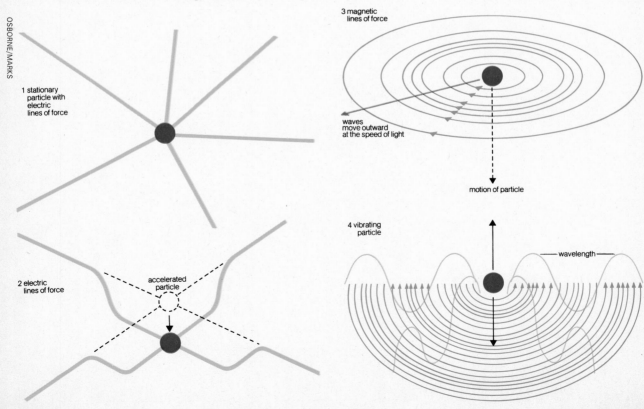

OSBORNE/MARKS

1 stationary particle with electric lines of force

2 electric lines of force

accelerated particle

3 magnetic lines of force

waves move outward at the speed of light

motion of particle

4 vibrating particle

wavelength

silver metal, and the developing process enhances this reaction to produce an image.

Devices like the EXPOSURE METER on a camera also rely on the energy of light quanta, which raise the energy of electrons in the detector. This change is then shown on a meter. Some detectors of this type can be made to respond even to the lower energy of infra-red photons. Alternatively, electrons released by the light from the cathode of a PHOTOMULTIPLIER TUBE or TV camera are accelerated by an electrostatic field to produce an electric current which can then be amplified.

Ultra-violet
At wavelengths shorter than 390 nm is the ultra-violet, which extends down to 1 nm. This radiation is emitted by extremely hot bodies, but the temperatures needed are higher than the boiling point of all substances so ultra-violet is produced this way only in very hot stars.

On Earth ultra-violet is produced in a different way. The electrons in atoms and molecules can have only certain energies, and when they move from one energy state to another they emit the excess energy as electromagnetic radiation. This radiation will occur at particular frequencies corresponding to the energy changes in the atom. Many atoms will produce frequencies which are in the ultra-violet part of the spectrum, one example being mercury, which is used in 'sun-tan' ULTRA-VIOLET LAMPS. Atoms can also produce wavelengths which lie in the visible spectrum by this process. The colour of sodium street lights is due to an energy change in the sodium atom which results in radiation whose wavelength corresponds to yellow light.

X-rays
Higher frequencies still can be produced by suddenly decelerating a stream of electrons. In a typical apparatus the electrons are suddenly stopped by hitting the metal anode. The wavelength of the radiation emitted can range from 10 nm down to 0.001 nm, depending on how fast the electrons are travelling. These waves are known as X-rays.

X-radiation is easily detected by a photographic plate: a hospital X-ray examination is recorded on ordinary photographic emulsion. If a picture is not needed, a PARTICLE DETECTOR can be used. These come in various forms (one being the GEIGER COUNTER) but the principle is the same for all.

Gamma rays
Shorter wavelengths than these can be reached only by relying on the natural random processes in the nucleus of an atom. A proton in the nucleus can change its energy state, just as the electron in the atom does, but the frequencies emitted will be much higher, corresponding to wavelengths less than 0.01 nm. These waves are called gamma rays, and are the shortest electromagnetic waves yet detected.

Although the character of electromagnetic radiation changes so dramatically from one end of the spectrum to the other, and the apparatus used to produce and detect it at different frequencies appears so dissimilar, it is worth remembering that it is basically one phenomenon, the disturbance in the electric and magnetic fields of a charged particle when it is accelerated.

Left: A stationary charged particle (1) has electric lines of force which are kinked when the charge is accelerated (2). This also produces a bunched wave in the magnetic lines of force (3). A vibrating charge creates continuous waves in both the electric and magnetic fields (4), at right angles to the direction of motion. Below: the whole electromagnetic spectrum. Different detectors are needed for each part: the eye can distinguish between the colours of the visible region, for example, while a radio tuner is needed to discriminate between the frequencies of the radio spectrum. Two 'black body' curves are superimposed, showing the wavelengths of power emitted by the Sun (6000°C) and an electric fire (2000°C).

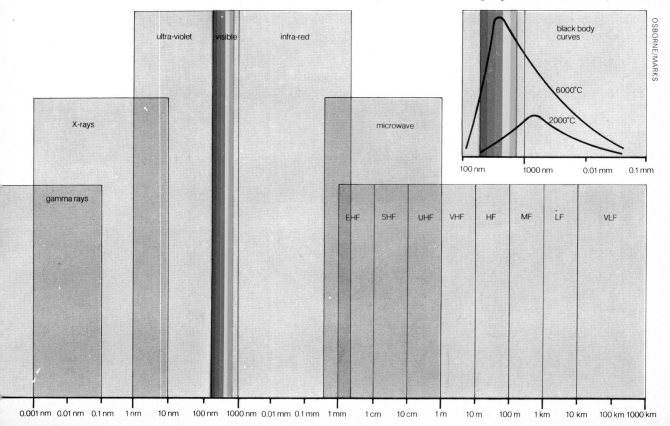

ELECTROMAGNETISM

If a permanent magnet attracts a piece of iron or steel, that is a purely *magnetic* action. If a battery sends electric current through a wire so as to heat it, that is an *electric* effect. But wherever an action takes place involving both magnetism and electricity, such action is said to be *electromagnetic*. There are therefore many manifestations of this phenomenon which was first discovered by the Danish Scientist OERSTED and greatly enlarged by the subsequent work of FARADAY in the first part of the nineteenth century.

One common manifestation of electromagnetism is that a current flowing in a wire produces a magnetic field—this is the operating principle of an electromagnet, and can be harnessed to produce motion in ELECTRIC MOTORS through the attractive and repulsive forces of magnetic fields. When a magnet (either a permanent magnet or electromagnet) is moved near an electrical conductor, turbulent EDDY CURRENTS are induced in the conductor and it experiences a 'dragging' force. This dragging force can be used to produce motion, and conversely, the eddy currents can be harnessed to produce a useful electric current (such as in ALTERNATORS and DYNAMOS). This is an example of a moving magnetic field producing an electric current.

A more complex example of electromagnetism is found in devices such as TRANSFORMERS where a *changing* magnetic field produces a current. Here, two coils of wire are placed close together. When a changing current (changing in amplitude and-or direction) flows through one coil a changing magnetic field is produced, which induces a voltage in the second coil. If this second coil is included in any kind of electric CIRCUIT a current flows.

Understanding by analogy
These phenomena are not fully understood by man. But in order to exploit them, we devise mental models called 'analogues' to help us to obtain at least an appreciation and a hope that through this means we may learn to design better machines by using a phenomenon which is no more understood than is GRAVITATION.

For electric circuits we imagine that electrons flow in wires in much the same way that water flows in a pipe. We know that pressure is needed to make water flow so we invent an electrical pressure and call it *electromotive force* (emf) or voltage. The convenience of this analogue is that it allows us to use the equivalent of the frictional resistance in the water pipe which increases in proportion to the length of the pipe but decreases in propor-

Below: Joseph Henry (1797–1878) designed this lifting mechanism for heavy loads. The lifting force is provided by an electromagnet. Henry did much work on electromagnetism.

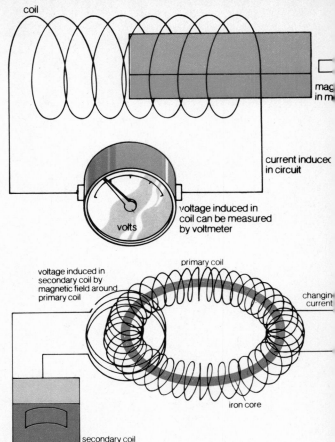

coil

mag in m

current induced in circuit

voltage induced in coil can be measured by voltmeter

volts

voltage induced in secondary coil by magnetic field around primary coil

primary coil

changin current

iron core

secondary coil voltage measured on voltmeter

volts

Top: when a magnet is moved through a coil of wire, a voltage is induced which can be measured on a voltmeter.

Above: a transformer consists of two coils wrapped around a common 'magnetic circuit'—a ring of iron. When a changing voltage is applied to the terminals of the primary coil a current is set up which creates a magnetic field. This induces a voltage in the secondary coil.

Below: an attempt to construct a physical picture of an electromagnetic wave. The electric part E oscillates in one plane and the magnetic field H at right angles to this. It travels at the speed of light.

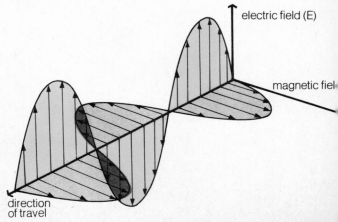

electric field (E)

magnetic fiel

direction of travel

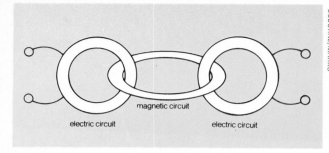

electric circuit   magnetic circuit   electric circuit

Above: the interlinking of electric and magnetic circuits is funda-mental to our way of thinking about electromagnetism. This diagram illustrates electric and magnetic circuits in a transformer.

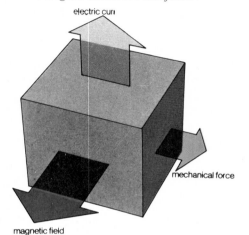

electric curr

mechanical force

magnetic field

Above: in electromagnetic reactions, the directions in which electric current, magnetic field and mechanical force interact are all at right angles to each other. Parallel components of these do not interact.

Right: when trying to design the best electromagnetic machines, the engineer tries to make both the electric and magnetic circuits as short as possible. This means that the least energy is wasted in each type of circuit. He also tries to make the cross-sectional areas as large as possible—this increases the area of interaction of the two circuits and enables the device to work efficiently.

electric (copper) circuit

magnetic (iron) circuit

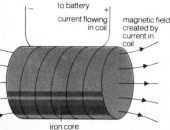

to battery
current flowing in coil
magnetic field created by current in coil
iron core

Left: this is the most simple of all electromagnetic devices. A coil of wire wrapped around an iron bar (core) and carrying an electric current makes the bar act like a permanent magnet.

tion to its cross sectional area. Then, by another analogy, we can invent a *magnetic circuit*, in which the driving pressure is called *magnetomotive force* (mmf) and the 'substance' which it drives around the circuit is even less 'real' than the flow of electrons in an electric current. We call it *magnetic flux*. Many authors and teachers declare that, despite its name, flux does not flow. The fact is that it does not exist, except as a human concept, and the only 'right or wrong' about its flow is to be judged on whether the concept is useful to a particular individual. For some, it is more profitable to think of flux as merely being 'set up' because it represents only *stored* energy, and not a continuous loss of power as is the case when electric current flows in a wire. For others, the analogue is more profitable if flux is considered to be a more precise analogue of electric current so that a magnetic circuit can be given the properties appropriate to INDUCTANCE and CAPACITANCE in an electric circuit.

Linking electric and magnetic circuits   When discussing electric motors, generators and transformers, it is essential to note that each machine includes at least one electric and one magnetic circuit. Since there is no simple equivalent in magnetic circuits to the insulating materials of electric circuits, it is usual to design a machine with only one magnetic circuit but two or more electric circuits. Moreover, for the same reason, electric circuits in machines are usually multi-turn coils of relatively thin, insulated wire. Magnetic circuits tend to be single-turn, short and fat.

The subject of electromagnetism can therefore be expressed as the *linking* of electric and magnetic circuits. In such a linking the driving pressure from one circuit is seen to be derived from the flow in the other, and vice-versa. For example, in a transformer an alternating voltage (emf) across the primary windings produces an alternating current in the windings. This produces an alternating mmf in the magnetic circuit, which creates an alternating flux. The alternating flux induces a voltage in the secondary windings, which, if connected in an electrical circuit, produces current.

Vector quantities   The commodity we seek to produce in an electric motor is force which arises as the result of multiplication of flux by current, but it is no ordinary multiplication, for the only quantities of flux and current which are effective are those which cross each other at right angles. Quantities which have both magnitude and direction are called *vectors*, and when determining the interactions of vectors with each other the direction as well as the magnitude must be taken into account. In the above example, the force vector is the result of the *vector multiplication* of the flux and current vectors. Where the flux and current vectors are not at right angles to each other they must be resolved into parallel and right angular components, but it is always the right angular components which produce the force vector. Furthermore, the force vector is always at right angles to both the flux and current vectors.

Vector multiplication and, more generally, vector mathematics is only a form of 'shorthand' for handling quantities which have been shown experimentally to interact in this unusual way. This is another example of an analogue.

Electromagnetic radiation   The principles of electromagnetism are not limited to electric motor and generator design. ELECTROMAGNETIC RADIATION is the name given to a variety of phenomena to which we give different names depending on the context in which we study them. Thus gamma-rays, X-rays, ultra-violet radiation, visible light, infra-red (heat radiation) and wireless (radio) waves are all of the same nature

and can all be expressed in terms of a continuous interchange of magnetic and electric energy, each of which pulsates in a plane at right angles to the direction of travel of the radiant waves. All travel at the same speed, approximately 3×10^8 (300,000,000) metre/sec (about 186,000 mile/s). The only thing which distinguishes one kind of radiation from another is its wavelength (or frequency). The whole spectrum of radiation extends from very low frequencies with wavelengths of many miles, to incredibly high frequencies (of the order of over 10^{22}Hz (1 Hz = 1 cycle/second) and wavelengths less than a millionth of a millionth of an inch.

The study of electromagnetism is therefore basic to the whole of physics, if not to the whole of science. The Earth receives most of its energy from the sun by electromagnetic radiation. The average private family house in Britain contains between 30 and 100 electromagnetic devices (although the higher numbers generally occur where there are several children, each of whom has battery-powered toys). Electromagnetism is basic to the operation of radio and television sets, car ignition systems, radar, electric systems, microscopes, electric motors and generators, telephones and many other inventions.

ELECTROMETER (see electrostatics)

ELECTROMOTIVE FORCE (EMF) see circuit, electrical

Left: Faraday's disc dynamo. The disc is made of copper and positioned within the arms of a horseshoe electromagnet. Contacts are made with the disc at its centre and periphery by means of 'brushes' and connected externally to an electrical circuit. When the disc is rotated, a voltage is induced in the disc between the brushes.
Below left: a 52 inch (1.35 m) diameter lifting electromagnet. This can handle over a ton of metal (shown here with medium steel scrap).
Below: electric traction motor (1900). The motor, like the dynamo, is an electromagnetic device. Its operation is based on the fact that a current carrying conductor experiences a force in magnetic fields.

ELECTRON

The electron, which is one of the constituent particles of all ATOMS, was discovered at the end of the last century in a series of experiments, the most famous being those of the Cambridge physicist J J Thomson in 1897. He came to the revolutionary conclusion that 'atoms are not indivisible for negatively electrified particles can be torn from them by the action of electrical forces'. This dispelled the belief that the atoms were the basic building blocks of all matter.

Thomson had set up an electric field in an evacuated glass tube and detected something coming from the negatively charged electrode (cathode), travelling towards the positively charged electrode (anode) and lighting up the glass of the tube where it struck. It proved possible to bend these 'cathode rays' with magnetic fields and, in this way, to show that they were negatively charged and lighter than any atom (in fact about one two-thousandth of the mass of the hydrogen atom, which is the lightest of the atoms). The principle and the equipment, in more advanced versions, of Thomson's experiment puts the electron at our service today in the CATHODE RAY TUBES of the television set.

The electrons exist in the atom orbiting around the nucleus. They are held there by the electromagnetic attraction existing between the negative charge carried by the electron and the positive charge of the nucleus, just as the moon is held in orbit by the gravitational attraction between it and the earth. In the heavier atoms as many as ninety electrons can be swirling in a cloud around the nucleus and, in moving from one orbit to another, they are the source of energy which gives us light and X-rays. Also it is the behaviour of the electron clouds of the different atoms and the way the clouds link together (see BOND, CHEMICAL) that gives us the chemical properties of all matter.

The electron is the carrier of ELECTRICITY, passing with comparative ease through the lattice arrangements of atoms in metals. The unit of electric charge carried by a single electron is, however, very small. A million, million, million of them are in the electric current flowing through a 100 watt bulb in a second. Other figures which illustrate the small scale of this particle which plays such an important role in our world are: the mass of the electron is one ten thousand million million million millionth of a gramme and its radius is one ten million millionth of a centimetre.

One of the revolutionary developments in physics in this century involved the realization that an electron can either behave like a particle or like a wave. As particles they can do such things as knocking silver halide molecules about (thus leaving traces in photographic emulsions) and be accelerated by electric fields. As waves they can form 'diffraction' patterns when passed through foils—like the patterns on the surface of a pond when waves ripple out from dropping in two stones at different places. With the wave-type behaviour it is even possible for the electron to pass through barriers which, looking at the electron as a particle, are impenetrable. This is still one of the puzzles of modern physics.

Below: Millikan's famous oil drop experiment, designed to determine the basic charge of an electron. Minute oil droplets, sprayed from an atomiser between two capacitor plates, acquire a small charge from friction on the nozzle. These drops will move under the force of an electric field applied across the plates and reach a final velocity which is proportional to the strength of the field and also to the electric charge on the oil droplet. Other factors will also influence this velocity such as gravitational force, air resistance and the oil's density. At a certain point the electric field will exactly counteract these forces and the drop is suspended. By repeating this experiment many times, a series of values for the charge is reached. These are integral multiples of the charge of a single electron.

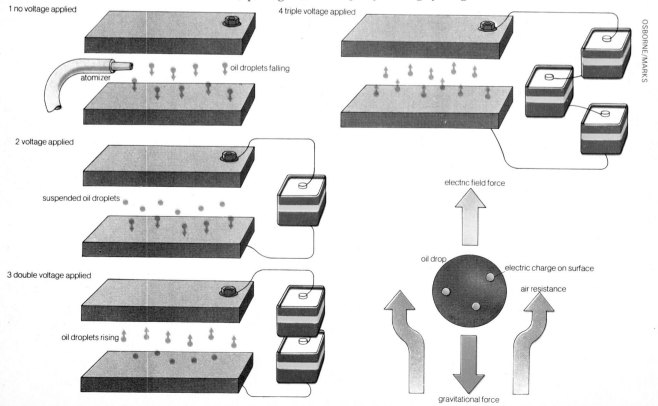

1 no voltage applied
atomizer
oil droplets falling

2 voltage applied
suspended oil droplets

3 double voltage applied
oil droplets rising

4 triple voltage applied

electric field force
oil drop
electric charge on surface
air resistance
gravitational force

OSBORNE/MARKS

ELECTRONIC NEWSCASTER

The 'electronic' (actually electric) newscaster is a machine for displaying news bulletins, weather reports and advertisements on a long illuminated screen. The screen itself is made of rows of filament lamps which are illuminated in sequence so that the display moves along the screen from right to left.

The message to be displayed is first punched on to a long strip of strengthened paper, which is then joined to form a continuous loop. The loop is next loaded on to a machine which reads the information from the strip and controls the lights on the screen. There are two of these machines, one for the news tapes and one for the advertising tapes, and the newscaster reads from each one in turn.

Tape preparation The pattern of the holes punched in the tape corresponds to the pattern of lights to be shown on the screen, and there is a separate track on the tape for each of the colours that can be displayed on the screen (usually red, blue, green and white). If a character is to be shown in one colour only, it is punched only in the track for that colour, but various colour effects can be produced by punching a character into more than one track at a time. The punch dies are controlled by perforated metal plates; the perforations are drilled so that the shape of the character is formed by the undrilled portion. The dies are arranged in a matrix and the plate is pulled down on top of them so that the undrilled part forces the dies beneath it through the paper. The remaining dies pass through the perforations and so are not pushed down to punch the paper.

The tape for the advertisements is about $13\frac{3}{4}$ inches (35 cm) wide to accommodate the four colour tracks, but the news tape is only about $3\frac{1}{2}$ inches (9 cm) wide because the news is displayed in one colour (white) only.

A single hole (known as the cue dot) is punched near the edge of each tape, 22 inches (56 cm) before the end of the message, to signal the equipment to change over from reading that tape to reading the other one. A space of 36 inches (91 cm) is left unpunched on the tapes between where the message ends and the point where it begins again, so that there is no overlap between the messages on the two tapes during the changeover. In addition to the normal alphanumeric characters it is possible to punch the tapes with trade marks and other designs.

Readers and screen The tape is read by passing it between a bath of mercury and a head assembly. The head assembly contains rows of contacts which each connect with a light on the display screen, the circuit being completed between the contacts and the mercury through the holes in the tape. The tape moves from right to left across the head; the first set of contacts connects with the first row of lamps on the screen, the second set with the second row, and so on in sequence across the head, which is about 23 inches (58 cm) long. The head for the advertising tape has a row of contacts for each colour track, but the news tape head has only one row which connects with the white lamps on the screen. Some types of newscaster use photoelectric cells instead of the mercury bath arrangement for reading the tape.

The lights on the screen are small filament lamps (40 V AC, 2.5 W) covered by coloured plastic domes, and with four basic colours of lamp a total of fifteen character colours can be obtained by mixing. The largest newscaster in Europe, at Leicester Square, London, has a total of 30,000 lamps on its two 75×5 foot (23×1.5 m) screens, which are protected from fire by a sprinkler system fitted above them. The lamps need replacing at a rate of about fifteen per day, and the total power consumption of the system is approximately 9 kW.

Top: the newscaster in Leicester Square, London. The twin screens are fabricated from panels 5 ft (1.5 m) high and 4 ft (1.2 m) long, with the lamps arranged in vertical rows of white, green, and alternating red and blue lights. The vertical spacing between lamps is arranged to give clusters of lights, and each cluster contains two of each colour which produces an even display effect with no voids in the letters.

Above left: one of the drilled plates used to control the pattern of the punch dies when preparing the tapes.

Above right: punching an advertising tape. On this machine the four colour tracks are, from top to bottom, blue, green, red and white.

NPL/PHOTOS: MIKE ST MAUR SHEIL

Top right: the advertising tape reader. The tape is lying across the mercury bath, and the read head has been tilted back to show the four rows of contacts.

Centre right: part of the news tape reader, showing the tape passing between the read head and the mercury bath.

Right: a close-up of a newscaster screen; the arrangement of the coloured lights can be clearly seen.

ELECTRONICS

Electronics is the branch of science and engineering concerned with the understanding, development and applications of electronic devices. On the theoretical level it involves a large number of scientific disciplines including PHYSICS, CHEMISTRY, THERMODYNAMICS, QUANTUM mechanics and MATHEMATICS.

As an applied science it has grown out of electrical engineering which is concerned with every aspect of ELECTRICITY: its generation, control, distribution, storage and applications. Today, the electronics industry is an integral part of modern industrial life and is becoming more and more important in the underdeveloped parts of the world as well. For example, today there are more than 800 million TRANSISTOR radio sets in use throughout the world.

Electronic devices   An electrical CIRCUIT is designed to control electric current for a particular purpose and consists of components, or elements, with specific electrical characteristics. The most common components found in electrical circuits are RESISTORS, CAPACITORS, INDUCTORS, SWITCHES and POTENTIO-METERS and they can be used separately or together in a variety of ways. Electronic circuits are a development from electrical circuits and include electronic devices, such as thermionic VALVES [vacuum tubes], gas filled tubes and SEMICONDUCTORS.

Thermionic valves and related devices   With the advent of the thermionic valve [vacuum tube] and other related devices, the scope of applications was further increased and new potentials realized. Vacuum tube devices are a particular 'family' of electronic devices and consist basically of two electrodes sealed within an evacuated glass tube. One electrode, called the *cathode,* is constructed from an alkali metal

such as caesium which readily 'boils off' electrons when heated. The other electrode, called the *anode,* is usually maintained at a positive voltage with respect to the cathode so that these electrons are drawn away and accelerated towards the anode. In this way a current flows through the device.

This particular vacuum tube is called a DIODE because it contains only two electrodes. These have the property that an electron current can only flow in one direction as no electrons are available at the anode for current to flow in the other direction, so the diode is used to rectify alternating (AC) currents.

A *triode* valve is a diode with an extra (third) electrode placed between the anode and cathode. This third electrode is in the form of a mesh or *grid* which allows electrons to pass through relatively unhindered. When, however, a voltage is applied to this grid the electron current flowing through the device is modified or controlled—hence the term 'valve'. Small changes in grid voltage can produce large charges in cathode-anode current.

In some applications two or more grids are required, which can independently control the electron current. Such thermionic valves are called tetrodes (2 grids), pentodes (3 grids) and so on.

The CATHODE RAY TUBE (CRT) is a vacuum tube device designed to produce a visual display. Again, electrons are boiled off a hot cathode and drawn towards the (positive) anode, but in the centre of this is a hole through which some of the electrons can pass in the form of a beam. At the front of the CRT is a fluorescent screen which glows when bombarded with electrons. Using a grid between anode and cathode to control the intensity of the beam, a focusing system to focus the beam to a point at the screen, and deflection plates to move the spot on the screen around, a useful display can be created.

The klystron, magnetron and travelling-wave tube are other types of thermionic vacuum tube devices for the amplification of very high frequency signals to high output powers (see MICROWAVE DEVICES).

Gas filled tubes   The most common application of gas filled devices is in light displays such as DISCHARGE TUBES, fluorescent lights, neon lamps and so on. These are, however, not generally described as electronic devices because they do nothing more than provide light. There is no clear distinction here, as, for example, the particular characteristics of a gas discharge makes it useful in overload voltage protection equipment. When a certain critical voltage is reached (the *striking* voltage) a discharge is formed and it acts as a low impedance 'short-circuit', protecting any surrounding components (electronic or otherwise). Also, at a certain magnitude of discharge current these devices exhibit a negative resistance. That is, as the current is increased the voltage between the electrodes drops. This voltage-current characteristic is opposite to a resistor. Such devices can be used in OSCILLATOR circuits.

Gas filled diodes work on a similar principle to vacuum tube diodes insofar as the cathode is designed to emit electrons. In gas filled diodes, however, current is conducted through the gas rather than as a beam of electrons. Also, electrons can be knocked out of the cathode by bombardment with positive gas IONS (atoms which have lost an electron).

The mercury arc rectifier (diode) is another similar device.

WIRELESS WORLD

Left: early crystal receiver set. It consists of an induction coil with slide contact and a cat's whisker diode demodulator mounted on top. With the slide contact, the circuit could be tuned to a station.

Conduction takes place in a pure mercury vapour produced by a spark heating device adjacent to a reservoir of mercury which also forms the cathode. A carbon electrode is commonly used for the anode. Such devices are used where large AC currents need to be rectified.

Other gas filled devices include the thyratron—a type of triggered diode with three terminals rather like a triode valve—and stepping, or counter, tube devices such as the Dekatron. Here, a glow discharge between a cathode and an anode can be made to travel around a numbered tube and so produce a numerical display (see COUNTING DEVICES).

Semiconductor devices

By far the most important area today is semiconductor electronics. But although the semiconductor transistor is a relatively modern invention, semiconducting materials (that is, materials which do not properly conduct but which cannot be classified as insulators) have been known since the beginning of this century.

The 'cat's whisker' diode was an early invention consisting of a fine wire contact on the surface of a semiconductor crystal such as carborundum or silicon. It is the junction between the wire and the crystal which produces the diode action.

Copper oxide, selenium and tantalum rectifiers (known as metal rectifiers) can also be classified as semiconducting devices.

Silicon and germanium semiconductors are the most common electronic devices available today. As pure materials, silicon and germanium make poor conductors (except at elevated temperatures) but when a small amount of impurity is added—called a 'donor'—the conducting characteristics change completely.

In its simplest form, the germanium or silicon diode consists of a thin slice of the basic material alloyed on one surface with a donor material (antimony in the case of germanium) to produce an *n-type* semiconductor. This is a material with sufficient electrons in the conduction band (or shell) surrounding each atom nucleus for electron conduction to occur through the material. The other surface is alloyed with another material (for example, indium in the case of germanium) creating a *p-type* semiconductor. This has a deficiency of electrons in the conduction band which can be considered as 'holes' or vacancies for electrons and as such are positive. These positive 'holes' can move easily through the material under the influence of an electric field as can electrons in an n-type material.

Between the n-type and p-type sections is 'the junction'—a region where neither holes nor electrons can easily move—which acts as a barrier to the flow of current. When the device has a voltage applied across it in one direction, the barrier is reduced and current flows. With the voltage reversed, the barrier is increased and no current flows—this is the diode action.

The transistor consists of a p-n-p or n-p-n sandwich with three leads, one to each section. The lead to the middle section (known as the base—equivalent to the valve grid) can be used to control the flow of current between the two outer sections (known as the collector and emitter—equivalent to the anode and cathode of a valve). As such, transistors act rather like triode valves and are useful in a multitude of situations including amplifier (analog) and switching (digital) circuits.

The thyristor consists of a p-n-p-n sandwich with three external connections—anode, cathode and gate. This device behaves like a conventional p-n junction diode when it is 'triggered' by a current pulse via the gate terminal connected to the inner p-type section. Thyristors are sometimes called silicon controlled rectifiers (SCR), behaving in a similar manner to thyratrons, and are particularly useful in power control systems such as ELECTRIC MOTOR control circuits.

All these devices are available in a variety of shapes and sizes for specific applications and through research and development are constantly being modified and improved.

History of electronics

The study of electricity and electromagnetism flourished with the discovery of a continuous source of electric current—the BATTERY. This occured in 1800 when Alessandro VOLTA invented the 'voltaic pile'. For the next half century various electrical and electromagnetic devices were developed—one important invention being the TELEPHONE pioneered by A G BELL in the 1870s.

The development of electronic equipment was significantly concentrated on communications systems where some means was required for amplifying weak telegraph and telephone signals, and the triode valve proved to be the answer. Lee de Forest announced this discovery in 1906, two years after Sir John Ambrose FLEMING had developed the diode. It was not until 1911, however, that the triode was considered as a useful current amplifier. In 1912, feedback circuits were employed in AMPLIFIERS and in 1913 feedback was used in an oscillator circuit.

As early as 1887, Heinrich HERTZ had demonstrated the physical existence of electromagnetic waves and in 1895 Guglielmo MARCONI demonstrated a primitive form of RADIO communication (radio telegraphy). For the transmission of speech, however, a source of high frequency AC voltage is required, which stretched electromechanical systems to their

Above: this is an electronic circuit composed of discrete components including transistors (silver), diodes (small pink), capacitors (bulbous red), and resistors (brown body) mounted on a board.

limit. In 1900 a high frequency ALTERNATOR was used in transmitters which sent speech signals a distance of 25 miles. With the introduction of the triode valve driven oscillator, however, the operating frequencies and transmission distances were increased and in 1916 speech signals were transmitted on medium and short wave frequencies. Regular BROADCASTING followed in 1920, with successful short wave radio transmissions over long distances demonstrated in 1922.

The old 'crystal set' receivers employing the 'cat's whisker' diode flourished during this period, but the cat's whisker device was invented back in 1901. Valve operated radio receivers became a practical proposition after the development of the high vacuum or 'hard' thermionic valve in 1914–15. This improved the characteristics and life-span of the valve.

Television was developed during the 1920s following the work of John Logie BAIRD, although the cathode ray tube that produces the picture was invented back in the late 19th century. That radio waves are reflected from the Heaviside-Kennelly layer—a region of the Earth's atmosphere (the ionosphere)— was demonstrated in 1924 and used to determine its height. This experiment led finally to the development of radar, but for this a means of generating very high frequency (microwave) high power radio waves was required. The magnetron, invented in 1921, proved to be the answer and was first applied in 1935, although it was a subsequent modification—the cavity magnetron—which lead to long range high accuracy radar.

In 1948 William Shockley announced the transistor and with this announcement semiconductor electronics came properly into existence. When electronically modifying and processing electrical signals, large currents and voltages are not necessary and can be a disadvantage. The first electronic COMPUTER, built during World War 2, consisted of more than 18,000 valves and the heat generated by these presented a major design problem. The size of the transistor, and its low power consumption and dissipation led to the practical digital computer—one of the most significant of electronic devices.

The need for increasingly compact electronic systems for such applications as space research has lead to microminiaturization and the semiconductor INTEGRATED CIRCUIT. One small slice of semiconductor material—called a 'chip'— and containing several thousand transistors, enabled great savings to be made in power consumption and removed overheating problems. Because of their size, capacitance and inductance effects could be greatly reduced, thus increasing the maximum operating speeds that could be obtained from these devices.

More recently, metal-oxide semiconductor (MOS) devices operating at very high speeds with minute power consumptions have been developed. These are the modern generation of integrated circuits, not more than a few millimetres in diameter. So small are the operating currents involved that it would be more true to say that they operate on charge transfer.

Semiconductor devices have been slower in development in the field of power electronics because of the problems of removing unwanted heat and the sensitive nature of semiconductor materials to temperature. Heavy duty rectifiers, thyristors and transistors have, however, been developed.

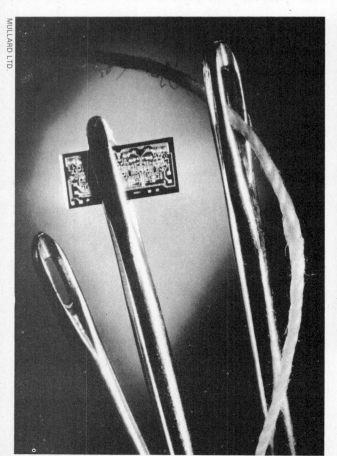

MULLARD LTD.

FERRANTI/PHOTO: PAUL BRIERLEY

Left: the smallness of the silicon chip, on which extremely complex circuits are made, is illustrated here. The circuit is a TTL (transistor-transistor logic) type for counting pulses in decimal. It will pass through the eye of a No 5 sewing needle.

Above: a hybrid circuit before encapsulation. This consists of several integrated circuits interconnected in a more complex unit.

ELECTRONICS IN MEDICINE

In response to the demand for improved knowledge and treatment of illness an increasing amount of electronic apparatus is being used in medicine today. The application of electronics to medicine now involves the use of such devices as AMPLIFIERS, stabilized power supplies, LOGIC CIRCUITS (including integrators and differentiators), RADIO frequency equipment, OSCILLATORS, pulse generators and counters, TRANSDUCERS, OSCILLOSCOPES, ULTRASONIC equipment, recording machines and COMPUTERS. Electronic apparatus used in medical care and treatment must be electrically safe, reliable, easily serviced, and have good hygienic and ERGONOMIC design. In addition, some components must be able to withstand sterilization. It has been possible to meet most of these requirements since the introduction of the TRANSISTOR and modern solid state devices.

The bulk of electronic equipment is located in hospitals where it is used in the diagnosis, treatment and administration of patients' illnesses. Electronic instruments in common use include a wide range of patient monitoring machines which display and record such factors as heart rate, body temperature, blood pressure and brain activity. The information from the monitoring equipment may be displayed at the patient's bedside or at a central nursing station, using a large-screen oscilloscope monitor, PEN RECORDERS, and sometimes multi-channel TAPE RECORDERS to record the instrument readings.

Electroencephalographs

The brain generates extremely small electrical currents which, when suitably amplified, produce distinctive traces that can be displayed on an oscilloscope screen or recorded on a pen recorder. The pattern of these brain waves depends on the activity of the brain, which in turn depends on the health of the patient and what he is doing. The general rhythms of the waveforms from a healthy brain are fairly consistent from one patient to another, and any irregularity or abnormality will show up as a distortion of the expected wave pattern.

The electrical signals from the brain are very small, typically around 100 microvolts, but they can be detected by electrodes fixed to the scalp or in some cases (such as during brain surgery) placed on the surface of the brain itself. These signals are then fed through high gain amplifiers in an *electroencephalograph* machine whose output signals are used to drive pen recorders or displayed on oscilloscope screens. The electroencephalograph (EEG) machine is widely used both in the diagnosis and detection of brain damage or illness, and in research into the functions of the different parts of the brain.

Electrocardiographs

The electrocardiograph (ECG) machine is related to the EEG machine but its function is the monitoring of the electrical signals given off by the muscles of the heart as they pump the blood around the body. When the ECG is used for monitoring the condition of a patient in hospital, a set of at least three metal disc electrodes covered on one face with a saline jelly are fixed to the patient's chest, jelly face down, with adhesive plaster. When sample ECG measurements are taken, as in an outpatient department, the electrodes are attached to the chest with rubber suction cups and readings may be taken from the arms and legs as well as the chest. A wire is connected to each electrode and plugged in to the ECG amplifier. The signals obtained are in the order of one millivolt, and the 'resting rhythm' of the heart is approximately 70 to 80 beats per minute. To display this signal satisfactorily the amplifier has a gain of not less than 1000 and is capable of reproducing exactly frequencies from 0 up to 100 Hz. To reduce unwanted interference, broad high frequency and very narrow mains frequency (50 to 60 Hz, depending on the country) filters are included. To protect the patient from any risk of electrocution, the part of the circuit closest to him (the *buffer* or input amplifiers) is isolated electrically and mechanically from the rest of the circuitry and thus also from the mains supply.

The signal is displayed on a built-in oscilloscope monitor and can also be used to drive a pen recorder. The ECG apparatus also includes a device which counts the number of heart beats and a meter to indicate the heart rate. ECG machines may be used to determine the condition of a person's heart during a medical check-up or if heart damage or disease is suspected, and they are also used to monitor the heart activity of a patient in hospital following a heart attack, accident or serious illness or surgery. In order to detect abnormalities in the ECG rhythm in such cases, the rate meter is filled with alarm circuits that will trigger an audible or visible alarm to

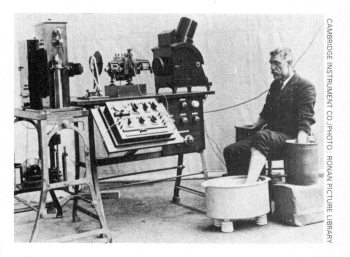

CAMBRIDGE INSTRUMENT CO./PHOTO: RONAN PICTURE LIBRARY

Above: an early electrocardiograph machine, made by the Cambridge Instrument Company in 1911. The first practical ECG machine was made eight years earlier in 1903 by Willem Einthoven.

KEN MOREMAN

Left: two ECG traces. The heart has four chambers (two atria and two ventricles) and the ECG displays the activity of these. The upper trace is a normal ECG; the large peaks show the ventricle activity, and each is preceded by a smaller peak showing the atrial activity and followed by another showing the myocardial repolarization (the relaxing of the heart muscles after each beat). The lower trace shows irregular atrial activity due to heart valve disease.

draw the nurse's attention to the change in the patient's condition. To assist the physician in deciding what abnormality has occurred the alarm circuit also triggers a pen recorder which will write out the ECG waveform (this is an advantage in that the pen recorder does not have to be running continuously while the patient is under observation).

Defibrillators If the heart ceases to function (cardiac arrest) it may be due to *fibrillation*, where the individual muscle fibres of the heart do not contract in a co-ordinated manner as they should. No characteristic waveform or rhythm can be detected in the ECG, the heart is 'shivering' and the patient's circulation is at a standstill. If undetected for more than five minutes this condition will result in the patient's death and so immediate remedial action must be taken to resuscitate him by using a *defibrillator*. A portable battery operated version of this instrument is kept available in hospitals and some AMBULANCES, since a cardiac arrest may occur anywhere at any time.

The purpose of the instrument is to induce the heart to restart its normal beating, and to achieve this two large electrodes are held manually on the chest wall over the heart and a high energy shock is given to the patient. This has the effect of contracting all the muscles in the chest, including the muscles of the heart, thus restarting the heart action. In some critical conditions it may be necessary to apply the shock several times. The defibrillator contains large value CAPACITORS that are charged from a stable DC voltage source, which gives them a potential of several kilovolts and an energy content of up to 500 Joules.

The capacitors are charged up, the electrodes applied to the chest wall, and the shock is triggered from a switch on the electrode handles. If the rhythm and waveform of the ECG are not completely absent the defibrillator may be linked to the ECG machine so that the electrical shock is synchronized with the muscular contraction of the heart.

Blood pressure monitors It is often important to measure the patient's blood pressure, as this gives an indication of the heart's capability to maintain an adequate blood circulation. This is normally done manually, but automated blood pressure monitors are in use in many hospitals. An inflatable rubber cuff is fitted around the patient's upper arm, and inflated to a preset pressure by the monitor to cut off the blood flow in the lower arm. The monitor then actuates the pulse *Korotkoff sound* detectors (these sounds are characteristic of the motion of blood through the main artery in the arm and named after their discoverer) and initiates a controlled leak of air from the cuff. The pressure in the cuff drops until it is equal to the peak pressure in the artery, and at this time the blood is just able to pass underneath the cuff and a pulse can then be detected by the monitor. The pressure reading in the cuff, which corresponds to the peak arterial pressure and is called *systolic* pressure, is stored by the monitor and displayed on a meter. The pressure in the cuff continues to drop until the Korotkoff sounds are detected and again the pressure reading is stored and displayed. This reading corresponds to the minimum or trough pressure and is called the *diastolic* pressure. To make these measurements use is made of either RELAY logic circuits or operational amplifier circuits to store and read out the systolic and diastolic pressures.

The detection of peak pressure is easily made since it is the first pulse to arrive, but detection of the diastolic point is more difficult and the various types of machine differ basically in how they achieve this measurement. The manual, semi and fully automatic cuff equipments all give erroneous readings both at very low (systolic below 80 mm of mercury) and high (systolic above 150 mm of mercury) pressures, so for a patient in a critical condition it may be necessary to use a more direct and accurate method of measuring the blood pressure.

To do this a very fine *catheter* (a nylon tube) is inserted into an artery and connected to a pressure transducer. The dome of the transducer and the catheter itself are kept free from blood by keeping a saline (salt) solution in them, which avoids blood clotting from causing false readings. The transducer has a pressure sensitive diaphragm, covered by an acrylic plastic dome, which usually has a four arm strain gauge bridge bonded to it or incorporated in it as in the case of semiconductor strain gauges.

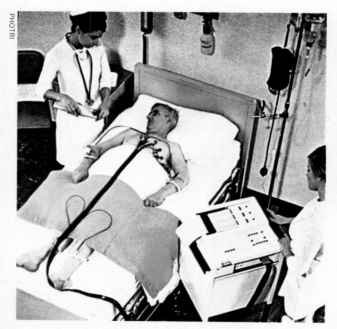

Above: this machine locates the position of brain tumours by detecting the gamma rays emitted from a radioactive substance injected into the bloodstream. The signals from the detectors are analyzed by computer to determine the position of the tumour.

Left: an electrocardiograph machine in use, recording signals from electrodes placed on the patient's chest, arms and legs.

The arterial pressure is displayed on an oscilloscope monitor and can be processed by peak and trough detection circuits to give the systolic and diastolic pressures. In some cases the mean value of the pressure is measured, to determine the Mean Arterial Pressure.

Patient monitoring systems

The ECG and the defibrillator may be used individually, or in the case of patients with more serious or long-term illnesses or injuries, such as those in intensive care units, they may be used in conjunction with other apparatus to provide a continuous monitoring of the patient's condition. Patient monitoring systems may comprise several individual machines separately connected to the patient, or the machines may be physically combined into one main unit such as a multi-channel physiological recorder (MCPR). In addition to providing the physician with information on the patient's condition the monitoring systems also contain alarms which alert the nursing staff to any dangerous changes that require urgent attention.

A typical monitoring system might contain instruments to display and record the ECG waveform, the pulse rate and blood pressure, the body temperature and the breathing rate, and some new systems are being developed which are connected to and supervised by a central computer system.

Other equipment

Modern operating theatres frequently use surgical *diathermy* apparatus. This equipment cuts tissue and coagulates bleeding vessels during surgery by passing a high radio frequency current through a small electrode at the site to be treated. The effect is achieved by instantly heating the tissue close to the electrode without affecting the surrounding tissue. Radio frequency is used since its effects are outside the threshold of the electrical stimulation of muscle tissue. Many theatres possess HEART-LUNG and KIDNEY MACHINES, in addition to X-ray and closed circuit TELEVISION equipment.

Outpatient departments use a wide range of electronic equipment, which includes portable diathermy equipment, ECG, EEG, and EMG machines, ultrasonic blood flow measuring apparatus and INFRA-RED temperature scanning equipment. The EMG machine (*electromyograph*) is used for investigating the electrical activity of stimulated muscle and nerve fibres.

The velocity of a patient's blood flow may be measured by fixing a transducer above a vein or artery, then transmitting an ultrasonic signal through it. The blood will reflect the signal, giving an 'echo' which can be detected. As the blood is moving the frequency of the echo will be different to that of the original signal due to the DOPPLER effect, and by comparing the two frequencies the velocity of the blood flow can be calculated. Ultrasonic echo detection is also used to create 'pictures' of the heart (echocardiography) and to detect brain damage and tumours, using a similar principle to the echo sounding equipment (ASDIC) used by ships.

Infra-red temperature scanning equipment scans an area of a patient's body to provide a picture of the surface temperature variations. An underlying tumour, such as in breast cancer, causes a localized increase in the surface temperature and so can be detected by this technique.

Laboratory support services use many forms of electronic apparatus, including BLOOD TYPING and clotting equipment, and automated biochemical machines which analyze urine and blood samples and serve to increase the speed with which sample analyses can be made.

In the treatment of certain heart conditions, the patient may be transferred to a unit in the X-ray department where, using image intensifier and closed circuit television techniques, catheters will be guided into the chambers of the heart to observe changes in them and to measure the output of blood from the heart. These observations, together with the results of ECG and other tests, can give the physician a complete picture of the behaviour of the heart.

Computers

The digital computer has many uses in the administration of hospitals, controlling such functions as medical records, staff payrolls, stock control and central collation of patient's clinical data. Increasing use is being made of both analog and digital computers in medical research, for example in the detailed analysis of abnormalities in EEG and ECG waveforms.

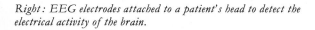

Above: the supervisory station of the patient monitoring system in the intensive care unit at St Luke's Hospital, New York. Signals from the monitoring equipment at each patient's bedside are displayed on the screens of this central console.

Right: EEG electrodes attached to a patient's head to detect the electrical activity of the brain.

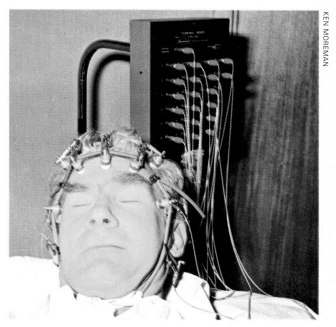

ELECTRON MICROSCOPE

The electron microscope was developed to examine specimens in much greater detail than had been previously possible using an ordinary MICROSCOPE, correctly known as the light microscope. It has proved extremely useful in studying metal as well as biological samples, such as viruses and cancerous tissue.

In 1873, a German physicist, Ernst Abbe (1840–1905) proved that in order to clearly distinguish between two particles situated closely together, the light source must have a wavelength no more than twice the distance between the particles. This therefore applies to adjacent points in a specimen.

The ability to clearly distinguish two particles is called *resolution*, which should not be confused with magnification. No matter how many times something is magnified if its image is blurred it will always be so. The wavelength of visible light is approximately 0.00005 cm (or 5000 angstrom units, one angstrom being 10^{-8} cm). Thus the minimum details resolvable under a light microscope would be 0.000025 cm (2500 angstrom units) apart.

In the search for a new type of microscope, X-rays, which have a much shorter wavelength than ordinary light, were considered, but a 'lens' to control X-rays could not be produced. Scientists began to study the electron, finding that accelerated electrons travel with a wave motion similar to that of light but over 100,000 times shorter. Researchers found that either electrostatic or electromagnetic fields could be used to control an electron beam, these 'lenses' behaving in much the same way as the glass lens does in focusing a beam of light. Gradually during the 1930s the electron beam and its control by magnetic lenses was developed to produce shadow pictures of specimens until in 1939 the first commercial electron microscope became available, capable of resolving 0.00000024 cm (24 angstrom units). Since this first commercial instrument, designers have worked towards higher resolutions until today's instruments are capable of resolving 0.00000002 cm (2 angstrom units) as a matter of routine.

The electron microscope is an example of accelerated twentieth century technology reaching a stage of development in less than twenty years, whereas it had taken 300 years to perfect the light microscope.

Transmission electron microscope

The first electron microscope was known as a transmission electron microscope because the electron beam was passed through an ultra thin sample. The variation in density of the specimen resulted in a variation in the brightness of the corresponding area of the shadow image. The transmission electron microscope consists of a vacuum column which is essential for the free passage of the electrons. A tungsten hairpin filament, the cathode, is heated to a point at which it emits electrons. By applying 20,000 to 100,000 volts between the cathode and the anode, the electron beam is accelerated down the column. (This system is called an electron gun.) Condenser 'lenses' control the beam size and brightness before it strikes the specimen, which is mounted on a 3 mm diameter copper mesh grid. The electron beam is focused and magnified by the objective lens before being further magnified and transferred on to a viewing screen by the intermediate and projector lenses. Most instruments cover the magnification range of $\times 50$ to $\times 800,000$. The screen is made of phosphorescent material (zinc-phosphide) which glows when struck by the electron beam, and beneath the screen is located a camera for recording the image. Micrographs are not usually recorded at the highest magnification of the particular electron microscope as it is easier to enlarge them later by normal photographic processes.

The limitation of the transmission electron microscope (as well as the conventional microscope) is that it can focus on only a limited depth of the specimen (depth of field).

Scanning electron microscope

In 1965 a second type of electron microscope became available with a depth of

A 1,000,000 volt electron microscope at British Steel Corporation's laboratory at Rotherham. It is about ten times as powerful as the first electron microscope.

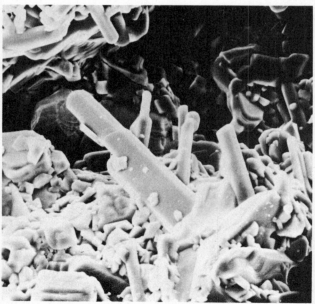

A scanning electron microscope photograph of a nest of crystals in a cavity in a fragment of moon rock. They are about 3.9 billion years old, and were formed when the rock was cooling.

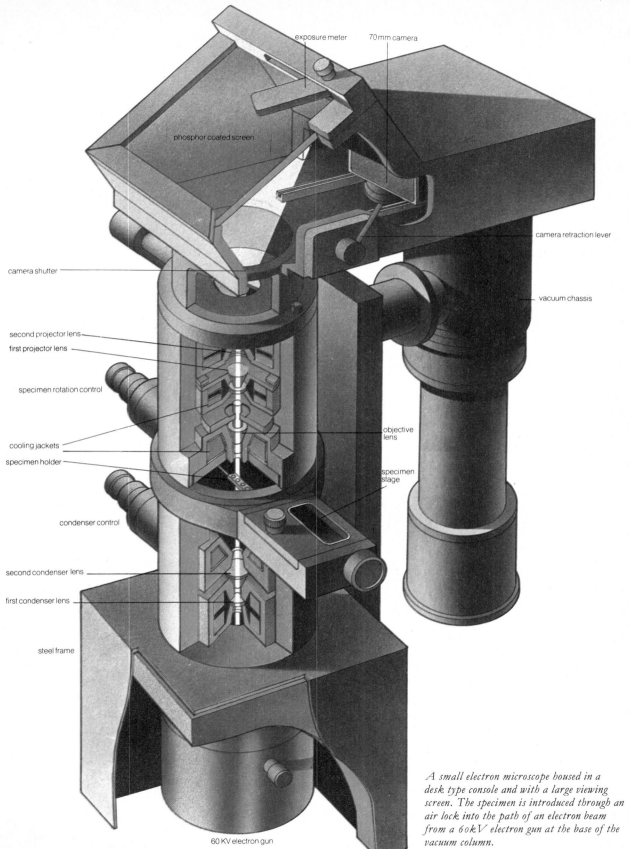

exposure meter

70mm camera

phosphor coated screen

camera retraction lever

camera shutter

vacuum chassis

second projector lens

first projector lens

specimen rotation control

objective lens

cooling jackets

specimen stage

specimen holder

condenser control

second condenser lens

first condenser lens

steel frame

60 KV electron gun

JOHN BISHOP

A small electron microscope housed in a desk type console and with a large viewing screen. The specimen is introduced through an air lock into the path of an electron beam from a 60kV electron gun at the base of the vacuum column.

field enabling the study of specimens in three dimensions. This new instrument was known as the scanning electron microscope. It employs a column very similar to that of the transmission instrument consisting of an electron gun and condenser lenses, which are used to 'bounce' the electron beam off the surface of the specimen. Situated in the condenser lenses are a pair of coils which deflect a small beam spot across the surface; linked to this scanning system is a CATHODE RAY TUBE (CRT), its electron beam being scanned across the screen in sequence with the beam in the microscope. The electron beam hitting the surface of the specimen drives off secondary electrons, which are drawn towards a detector which, via an amplifier, sends a signal to the grid of the CRT. The greater the number of electrons leaving the specimen the brighter the corresponding spot on the CRT. The magnification of the image depends on the relationship between the size of the area scanned and the size of the CRT, varying between 10 and 200,000 times. The image can be processed by the operator for brightness, contrast and display of either a negative or positive image. A conventional polaroid or roll film camera can be used to record the image.

The smaller the size of the scanned spot the higher the resolution achieved, but as the spot is decreased the energy that it contains decreases. A balance between the energy required to drive off the secondary electrons and the minimum spot size results in a resolution limit of 70 to 100 angstrom units in present day instruments.

Scanning transmission electron microscope

A third type of microscope first developed in the 1960s and commercially available in 1973 is the scanning transmission electron microscope, or STEM. It combines the most prominent features of its predecessors. The STEM has a new type of electron gun called a *field emission source*. The instrument scans the electron beam across the specimen, the electrons are collected by a detector and the image is produced through a conventional scanning display system. The field emission source enables a high energy beam, as fine as a few angstroms in diameter, to be produced. Thus the instrument is able to provide resolution as high as the transmission electron system with the flexibility and image display of the scanning electron microscope.

The largest electron microscope is a three million volt transmission instrument, so large that it is housed in its own building three storeys high. This massive instrument produces electrons of enormously high energy, enabling scientists to study specimens many times thicker than those which can be studied in conventional instruments. The ultra high voltages and the recently developed STEM will enable even more information to be obtained about specimens, using microscopy.

Specimen preparation

In electron microscopy specimen preparation is divided into two categories: transmission, including scanning transmission, and surface scanning. Biological transmission specimens usually undergo a complex preparation before being cut into very thin sections with an expensive instrument called an ultramicrotome; the conventional specimen thickness range being between 400 and 1000 angstroms. Metallurgical specimens are usually thinned down to less than 1000 angstroms by means of electrochemical polishing. Sometimes metal specimens containing particles can be examined as suitably transparent replica films, formed by deposition on to a thin plastic film that has been previously coated on a specimen grid. On the other hand, specimens for surface scanning are often examined with little or no preparation, but if a sample is non-conducting, a thin layer of gold may be deposited upon its surface to provide good contrast with the scattering of electrons.

ELECTRON OPTICS (see electron microscope)
ELECTRON–VOLT (see energy)

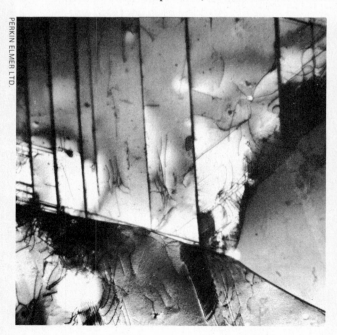

A specimen of stainless steel photographed at a five degree angle with about 200 kV of power. This reproduction represents a magnification of about 15,000 times the actual size.

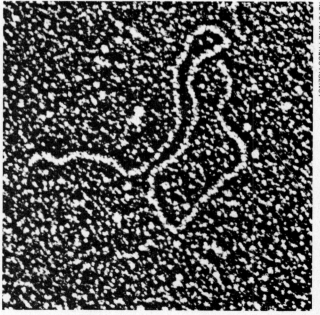

An epochal photograph: this is a picture of a gene, the basic component of heredity. It was taken at the Harvard University Medical School; the calculated length of the gene is 1.4 microns.

Top: an early silver plating process. The candlesticks were suspended in the electrolyte and current was passed. Additional silver salts (in the boxes on the side of the vat) were added as required.

Bottom: copper plating is usually done in either a cyanide bath or a sulphate bath. A typical cyanide bath includes cuprous cyanide, sodium cyanide and carbonate, and sodium thiosulphate as a brightener.

ELECTROPLATING

A wide variety of items, ranging from machinery to various household articles (see CUTLERY manufacture), are plated with metal coatings, usually to protect them against CORROSION and also to enhance their appearance, as in CHROMIUM plating (which incidentally involves first depositing a coating of nickel for corrosion protection followed by a thin overlay of chromium). Sometimes, however, as in the electro-galvanizing of small objects, such as nuts and bolts, the function is purely protective. Electroplating may also be used to impart certain other properties to a metal surface, such as hardness, wear resistance, and anti-frictional, electrical, magnetic or optical properties.

Coating thicknesses normally aimed at for decorative or protective purposes are in the region of 0.001 inch (25 micron), whereas greater thicknesses are sometimes required for specific engineering applications.

Principles of electroplating

In electroplating metal coatings are deposited on to conducting surfaces by making these the cathode in an electrolytic cell (see ELECTROLYSIS) with a suitable electrolyte containing heavy metal IONS—this is the plating metal. Under the influence of low voltage direct current, metal ions are reduced at the cathode to metal atoms which adhere to the object being coated, known as the basis metal. The quantity of current passed is proportional to the weight of metal deposited, according to FARADAY's law.

Simultaneously metal will go into solution at the anode (a

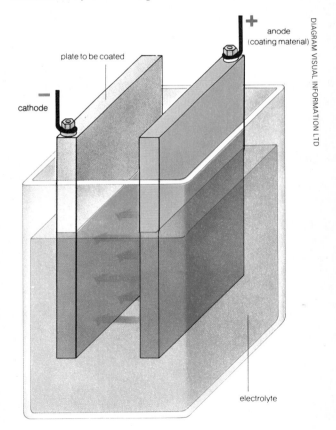

anode
(coating material)

plate to be coated

cathode

electrolyte

Above: electroplating. When an electric current is passed between the plates, metal from the anode passes into solution in the electrolyte and is deposited on the surface of the cathode.

sheet or bar of the plating metal), if the latter is soluble. In some instances, however, insoluble anodes have to be used for practical reasons: lead anodes are used in chromium plating solutions and conduct electric current but remain virtually unaltered—the chromium is removed from the solution and replaced by adding more chromic acid. In the case of a soluble anode, the weight of metal dissolved from it is proportional to the quantity of current passed. The electro-chemical reactions can be represented thus:

Cathode: metal ions + electrons→pure metal
Anode: pure metal − electrons→metal ions

Adhesion
In order to ensure good adhesion of the coating to the basis metal, there must be intimate linkage between the atoms of both metals, and for this reason the surface of the basis metal must be free from scale (caused by the formation of oxides on the metal surface during heat treatment and general production), grease and other deposits. Therefore appropriate preparation of items prior to plating is essential. It may include 'pickling' in dilute hydrochloric or sulphuric acids if scale or rust is present; mechanical treatment such as sandblasting; etching; solvent degreasing; chemical or electrochemical cleaning in alkaline solutions, or both.

Throwing power
One of the most important properties of an electroplating solution is its 'throwing power', which is its ability to deposit a metal coating of as nearly uniform as possible a thickness on a cathode surface, not all areas of which are equidistant from the anode. Good throwing power enables recessed portions of an article of complicated shape (to which less current penetrates) to be covered with a coating of adequate thickness. This is of particular significance in those cases where the basis metal has to be protected against corrosion. Complexed metal ion (ions formed by the combination of a simple metal ion with a neutral molecule) solutions normally possess a better throwing power than solutions of simple metal salts.

Commercial electroplating solutions
Commercial electroplating solutions consist of aqueous solutions of heavy metal and other salts to which various specific substances (normally organic compounds) have often been added to obtain coatings of desired properties (for instance, brightness, hardness, ductility, smoothness, adequate thickness in recesses and so on).

Although non-ferrous metals and alloys are often electroplated with coatings of various metals, the material most widely used as the basis metal for electroplating is steel. Most

metals below aluminium in the *electrochemical series* can be deposited from aqueous plating solutions. The electrochemical or electromotive series is a list of metals in which a metal higher in the series will replace one lower down from a solution of its salts. In order the main metals are sodium, magnesium, aluminium, manganese, zinc, chromium, iron, cobalt, nickel, tin, lead, (hydrogen), copper, mercury, silver, platinum and gold. (Metals before hydrogen release it from acids.)

Examples of metals which are electroplated commercially are mainly chromium and nickel but also include cadmium, cobalt, copper, gold, iridium, iron, lead, palladium, platinum, rhodium, silver, tin and zinc. For specific purposes, two or more metals are plated out simultaneously in the form of alloy coatings, examples being copper-zinc (brass), copper-tin (bronze), lead-tin, lead-tin-copper, tin-nickel and nickel-cobalt.

Decorative and protective coatings
Public taste demands that decorative and protective coatings should be bright, such as bright nickel-chromium finishes on car bumper bars, hubcaps and door handles, and various domestic fittings. In the past, bright finishes could be obtained only by mechanical polishing at various stages of the plating operation, which necessitated degreasing and cleaning after each stage. This was time-consuming and hence costly. For this reason, 'bright' plating solutions were developed, which contain specific organic additives which influence the topography (shaping) of the metal deposit in such a way as to produce a mirror finish.

Plant for electroplating
This can be automatic, semi-automatic, manually operated or barrel-plating plant.

In the first three categories, the work is treated individually, or at least is individually suspended on jigs. In the last case, bulk quantities of small items are handled without being mounted in any way. Automatic plants process articles mechanically through the various pre-treatment, plating and post-treatment stages, with complete elimination of manual handling. Such plants are used for mass production. In semi-automatic baths, transfer of the work from bath to bath is manually controlled, while in manually operated plant all stages of the plating operation are controlled by hand.

The size of plating vats can range from a few litres for the electrodeposition of such costly metals as gold, rhodium and platinum, to several thousand litres for the deposition of nickel and chromium in large automatic plants. The current used depends on the total surface area of the work being processed, and therefore it is usual to express it as current density, that is, current in amps (A) per unit area. The latter depends on the metal being deposited, bath composition and temperature, and can vary from some 0.002 A/cm² in the case of some noble metals, to 0.5 or more A/cm² for certain nickel solutions and chromium baths.

Barrel-plating comes into its own for plating large numbers of small items such as screws, washers, bolts, and so on. These are placed in a rotating barrel which is either perforated and immersed in the bath, with external anodes or (in the self-contained type) has an interior anode and contains not only the objects, but also its own solution. The advantages in the latter case are the small volume of solution required and also the ability to process really small parts which would drop out of normally perforated barrels.

Left: Unloading bright nickel and chromium plated oven racks from an automatic plating plant. After cleaning, the racks are nickel plated for 21 minutes, chromium plated for 5 minutes, rinsed and dried.

ELECTROSTATICS

Electrostatics is that branch of science concerned with the behaviour of electric charges at rest. This definition requires some expansion because the charges involved are in constant thermal agitation and, moreover, will move under the influence of an electric field. Electrical charges are therefore never completely 'at rest'.

Electrostatics is therefore best described as that part of the study of ELECTRICITY dealing with the individual interactions of charges and charged bodies. The other section of electricity dealing with the motion of electrical charges is called *electrodynamics*. Electrodynamics is in turn the basis for the study of electricity in its most common form—as electric current, the co-ordinated motion of electrical charges. ELECTROMAGNETISM originated as the study of the effects produced by the motion of electrical charges and as such is a development from electrodynamics.

Electrostatics and electricity

It was not until 1800 that a stable and regular source of electric current was devised. In that year, the Italian physicist Alessandro VOLTA invented the 'voltaic pile', which is the forerunner of the modern battery. This device, and its subsequent refinements, allowed scientists for the first time to study the effects of moving charges. Before the end of the same century, James Clerk MAXWELL had already formulated the laws of electromagnetism. This indicates the enormous impetus this single discovery gave to the study of electricity and electromagnetic phenomena.

Before the voltaic pile, the study of electricity was limited to electrostatic phenomena and the history of electricity before 1800 was simply the history of electrostatics. In particular, the phenomenon now known as *triboelectrification* where, for example, a comb passed through the hair will attract small pieces of paper, was discovered as far back as the sixth century BC by Thales, a Greek natural philosopher who noted that amber, when rubbed, attracted light objects. (Hence the

Above: a Wimshurst machine. It consists of two contrarotating glass discs with metal segments on their outer sides. These segments are charged as they pass two sets of brushes mounted at right angles (second set hidden). The charge is taken from the segments by two pairs of arms mounted at the sides and stored in two Leyden jars, which act as capacitors, mounted at each side. This method of charging, by triboelectrification, is also used in the electrophorus (below).

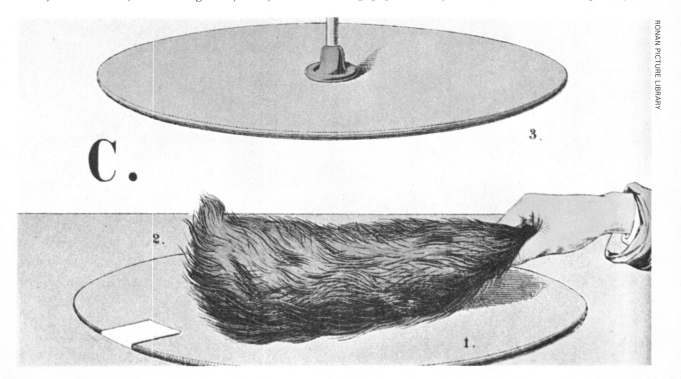

derivation of the word electron from the Greek *elektron,* meaning amber.)

Electrostatics hinges on the fact that both attractive and repulsive forces exist between charged bodies; like charges repel and unlike charges attract. For example, two electrons exhibit a repulsive force between them and in the atom it is the electrostatic attraction between the positively charged protons in the nucleus and negatively charged electrons that play a large part in binding the atom together. Indeed, the electrostatic force of attraction constitutes, in a sense, the very 'glue' of the universe. The gravitational force of attraction is, by comparison, much weaker.

Electrical charge

The most important charged particles in electrostatics (and in electricity) are electrons, which carry a negative charge. The unit of electrical charge is the *coulomb* and charge, like mass, length and time, is a fundamental unit or DIMENSION. An electron carries a negative charge of (minus) 1.6×10^{-19} coulombs (that is, approximately ten million million millionths of a coulomb). A proton (which incidentally is almost 2000 times as big as an electron) has the same magnitude of charge but is positive.

An electric current, which consists of flowing electrons, is measured in amperes (or amps for short), defined as one coulomb per second flowing through the conducting medium. Considering the extremely small charge carried by each electron this means an enormous number of electrons, approximately six million million million, flowing through the circuit per second.

Electrostatic force

The mathematical law that quantifies the attractive or repulsive force between charged bodies is known as Coulomb's law. This relates the magnitude of the force between the bodies to the charges carried by each, the distance between them and the electrical properties of the medium in which they are situated. This latter feature is expressed as the *permittivity* of the medium.

This law was theoretically deduced by the English scientist Joseph Priestley in 1766 but not established experimentally until 1785 when Charles COULOMB's work was performed. It is one of the 'inverse square' laws, since it states mathematically that the magnitude of the electrostatic force is inversely proportional to the square of the distance separating the two charged bodies. This means that doubling the distance between two electrons, for example, reduces the repulsive force between them by a factor of four.

Electrostatic force field

Because a force exists between two charged particles which are not apparently 'linked' in any physical way it is useful to consider each charged particle as being situated in an electrostatic force FIELD 'generated' by the other particle.

Around every charged body, therefore, there is said to be an electric field—this force field extending outwards from the charged body uniformly in all directions. It can be imagined as a series of concentric spheres around the body—the surface of each sphere representing an area of space where the effect of the charges is the same, but becoming progressively weaker away from the body.

This field theoretically extends to any point in space no matter how far from the charged body. In practice, however, the inverse square nature of the force field means that the electrostatic field around the charged body falls away very rapidly. An electron separated from a nucleus by only a few atomic diameters, for example, experiences very little attractive force towards the nucleus.

It is the existence of this force field around the positively charged nucleus of the atom that governs the behaviour of the orbiting electrons.

Potential and voltage

In a gravitational field a body can possess potential energy by virtue of its position in that field. If the body is allowed to fall that potential energy is transformed into kinetic energy as the body gathers speed. Similarly, a charged particle in an electrostatic field possess a 'potential' to move by virtue of its position in that field. Consider, for example, a body charged positively. An electrostatic force field, the magnitude of which is related to the magnitude of the charge on the body, exists around this body. The potential at any point in this field is defined as the amount of energy required to bring another body, this time of unit positive charge, from an infinitely large distance (where the repulsive force on it is for all practical purposes, zero) to that point. This can be seen to correlate to the idea of gravitational potential because this unit positive charge now possesses a potential to move. If it could be released from that position it would fly off under the influence of the repulsive force acting on it, and at infinity would possess kinetic energy equal to its former potential energy.

Similarly, the potential difference, or voltage, between two points in the field is measured by the amount of energy required to take this unit positive charge from one point to the other.

Applications

Devices which exploit electrostatics range from the very simple to the more complex. The CAPACITOR, although it is extensively used in electrical and electronic circuitry and can therefore be put to electrodynamic applications, is essentially an electrostatic device. Electron charges do not move through a capacitor, but are simply accumulated

Right: Cosmic rays create ionized particles (that is, charged particles) as they pass through the atmosphere. This gold leaf electroscope is an early instrument for detecting these charges.

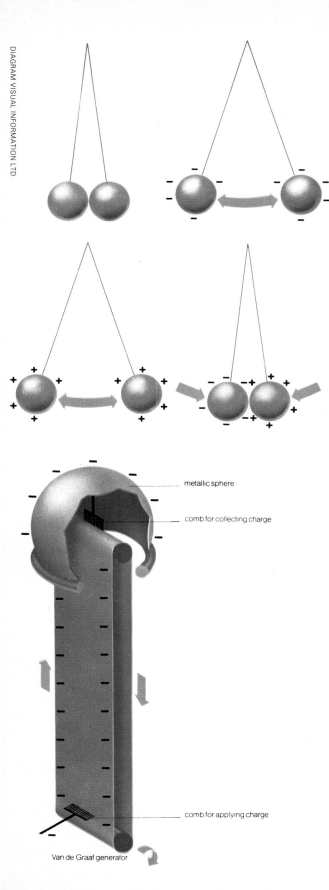

metallic sphere

comb for collecting charge

comb for applying charge

Van de Graaf generator

on its plates. One of the earliest electrostatic inventions, the Leyden jar, works on the same principle as the modern capacitor. It consists of a glass bottle that has had both its inner and outer surfaces covered in a thin metallic foil. The glass, which is a good insulator, acts as the dielectric, so that charge can be put onto the metallic foil and stored there simply by one side of the foil being touched repeatedly by a tribo-electrified object.

The gold leaf electroscope, which was invented in 1787, is another extremely simple instrument both in theory and practice. It essentially consists of two small pieces of gold leaf suspended from a conducting rod: a short tin bar is often used. At the other end of the rod a metallic plate is attached, and all the assembly below this plate is usually suspended in a sealed glass jar. When a charged object, such as a glass rod which has been rubbed with a piece of fabric touches the plate, charge flows onto the metallic rod down to the gold leaves. These gold leaves therefore receive the same sort of charge, and are forced apart because of the repulsive force between like charges. Hence charge can be detected by the separation of the two gold leaves, with the amount of separation providing a rough indication of the amount of charge. The more charge that is transferred to the leaves through the metallic plate and rod, the more powerful will the repulsive force be. The glass jar serves as an insulator against leakage of the charge into the air, so that the charge can also be accumulated on the electroscope. This instrument can still be found in laboratories.

More advanced laboratory demonstration devices for the generation and storage of electrostatic charge, such as the *electrophorus* and the *Wimshurst machine*, were developed in the 19th century in an attempt to devise an efficient and dependable source of charge. Both these instruments are far more efficient than the rubbing of a glass or plastic rod with silk or woollen cloth, but they are still based directly on the ability of a rubbed insulator to acquire nett charge.

Perhaps the most celebrated of all electrostatic machines is the Van de Graaff generator. This basically consists of a large hollow metal sphere mounted on top of a cylindrical column of an insulating material. An endless circulating belt made of some substance that has the ability to pick up charge and retain it is used to transfer charge from a charge generator at the base of the column to the surface of the sphere. Theoretically, any insulator could be used in the belt—just as any insulator can theoretically be triboelectrified—but in practice a rubberized fabric is usually employed. The size of the sphere means that an enormous amount of charge can be accumulated on its surface, and in this way potentials above ground of the order of millions of volts can be attained. This high potential is often utilized by connecting it to a type of PARTICLE AC-CELERATOR, to impart correspondingly great speeds to streams of electrons. These electrons, when subsequently directed towards target nuclei such as gold and tungsten, are sufficiently energetic to induce X-RAY emission from the nuclei they collide with. These are used, for example, in the treatment of superficial cancerous growths, the sterilization of surgical equipment from bacteria, and in the study of nuclear reactions.

Left: electrostatic force will hold apart two metal balls with the same charge and bind together two with opposite charges. In the Van de Graaff generator individual charges are 'sprayed' onto the surface of a moving belt from a comb—a row of sharp points held at a negative potential. These are collected at the top by another comb and transferred to the surface of a large sphere, building up a high voltage.

ELEMENT, chemical

A chemical element is the simplest form of matter; about 90 of them are found in Nature, and are numbered according to the number of electrons in their atoms. The heaviest element which is found in worthwhile amounts is uranium (atomic number 92), but in 1972 traces of plutonium (atomic number 94) were discovered. Still heavier ones can be created artificially at PARTICLE ACCELERATORS by firing subatomic particles (protons and neutrons) at a heavy element. Some of these particles can stick, at least for a short time, and chemical elements as high as atomic number 105 have been observed. The elements that concern us, however, are not the synthesized radioactive ones but those that form the building blocks of all substances. Some elements—usually the fairly inert ones such as gold, platinum, copper, nitrogen—occur free in Nature, but the majority are combined with other elements to form (sometimes highly complex) chemical COMPOUNDS or mixtures of compounds.

An element is in fact made up of the same type of atoms. So a bar of a pure metal, say the element copper, would consist of millions of individual copper atoms.

As long ago as the 6th century BC, the Greek philosophers developed theories of matter in terms of primary 'elements': water, air, fire and earth. It was believed that all known substances could be formed from these 'elements', either individually or together. It was BOYLE who coined the word element for simple, pure substances. Then in 1803 DALTON published the results of his investigations into the way elements combined in a 'law of chemical composition'. It was therefore possible to find out the relative weights of atoms from the proportions in which they combined in chemical compounds. For instance he found that eight parts by weight of oxygen and one part by weight of hydrogen were needed to produce water. Subsequently it was found that water is formed from two hydrogen atoms and one of oxygen so that the atomic weight of oxygen is 16 times that of water.

The chemical elements can be distinguished by their *atomic mass,* the quantity of matter contained in the respective atoms. For example, the lightest of the atomic masses is that of hydrogen with a mass of just over a million, million, million millionth (10^{-24}) of a gramme. These are rather clumsy units, however, and it is easier to use their *atomic weight* which is a number comparing the relative weight with that of the most commonly found ISOTOPE of carbon. (Isotopes of any particular atom have a different number of neutrons in the nucleus but chemically this makes no difference.) The atomic weight of carbon is taken as 12 precisely and the other elements are hydrogen, 1.008; helium, 4.003; oxygen, 15.999; uranium, 238.03 and so on. (Until 1961 atomic weights were based on taking the oxygen atom as 16 rather than carbon as 12.)

Another important figure is their *atomic number.* This corresponds to the number of protons in the nucleus of the atom. Thus hydrogen is 1, helium 2, oxygen 8, uranium 92 and so on. The atomic number also corresponds to the number of electrons in orbit around the nucleus of the atom, and it is the electrons which dictate all the chemical behaviour of an element.

Classification
Out of the total of 100 or so elements about 65 are classified as metals, 15 as non-metals and 6 as INERT GASES. The remainder are not easy to place; these include arsenic, germanium and antimony. Fortunately the chemical behaviour of these elements is not random. Distinct similarities exist such as the group of ALKALI METALS, namely,

lithium, sodium, potassium, rubidium and caesium and with other groups such as the HALOGENS (fluorine, chlorine, bromine, and iodine). When all the elements are listed in a table in order of atomic number, elements with similar characteristics (belonging to the same group) fall at regular intervals. The table is therefore known as the PERIODIC TABLE.

ELEMENTARY PARTICLE (see particle physics)

Below : if it were possible to break down all matter found on the Earth into its constituent elements their distribution would be as represented below. By far the most abundant elements are oxygen and silicon which occur widely in various rocks and minerals. On the other hand, the Universe itself consists of about 90% hydrogen atoms.

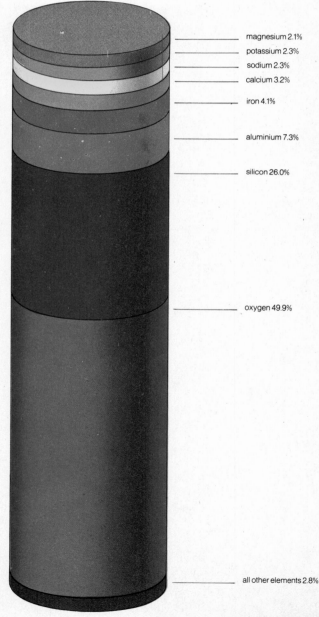

magnesium 2.1%
potassium 2.3%
sodium 2.3%
calcium 3.2%
iron 4.1%
aluminium 7.3%
silicon 26.0%
oxygen 49.9%
all other elements 2.8%

ELEVATED RAILWAYS

Ordinary railway trains can run on the ground, underground in tunnels, or on elevated structures. How they are built depends on whether the ground is level, the value of the land, intersections and many other factors.

When RAILWAYS are built in cities for RAPID TRANSIT, it is cheaper to build them underground than to clear buildings from valuable land to make room for them, even though tunnels are very expensive. The cheapest way to build railways in cities is to elevate them. The elevated structures can be built over the streets, where there is unused air space. With conventional railways, this makes the streets dark and noisy; nevertheless, elevated railways have been built in many cities, including Berlin, Liverpool and New York. In San Francisco, which is perhaps less congested than some cities, the land underneath the elevated structures has been landscaped and opened to the public as parkland.

One of the most famous elevated trains is in Chicago. Popularly known as the El, it began its existence in 1892 with steam power, but soon changed to electric. The elevated was consolidated with surface lines and in 1892 the famous Loop was built. Chicago's commercial downtown district has been called the Loop ever since, because it is defined by the elevated structure which encircles it.

The Loop structure follows the city streets, so extra short rolling stock, which was designed to turn corners sharply, had to be built. The solid axles, rigidly linking the wheels, cause the trains to make a lot of noise on curves. Chicago already has an underground railway [subway] as part of its transport system, built during World War 2, and current plans are to replace the elevated railway with more underground railway.

Trains are a very efficient means of moving people, and will continue to be used in cities if cities are to remain liveable. The elevated trains of the future are being designed faster than they can be built, but they will not be conventional trains: they will probably be MONORAILS. They will be quieter and cleaner than the elevated types, and probably operated by computers.

ELEVATOR (see lift)

Here are two views of the New York City elevated trains. The view below is the way they looked in 1884, pulled by a small steam locomotive; above, the way they look today, in Harlem. Today's elevateds are powered by electricity gathered from a third rail. Elevateds will probably be replaced by monorails.

ELEVATOR, grain

Bulk handled materials such as grain often have to be raised from one level to another using the least possible floor space and in the shortest time possible; this is achieved by the use of elevators.

There are various types of elevator in general use but the principal types are: the bucket, pneumatic, chain, and ARCHIMEDEAN SCREW elevators. They are often used in the BULK HANDLING of many other materials apart from grain.

Bucket type elevator This is the most common type of elevator and is used in a wide range of industries for handling materials as diverse as grain or limestone. Both the lift heights and capacities of these machines vary greatly, for example from 10 ft (3 m) lift height at 2 tons per hour, to as much as 200 ft to 300 ft (61 to 91 m) lift height at a rate of 2000 tons per hour in a large bulk grain intake system. It is most essential that the type of elevator used is matched to the material to be handled and this important function is achieved by using either a *centrifugal* or a *positive* type discharge unit. In the case of the centrifugal machines the material leaves the bucket at a tangent to its path, impelled by natural forces, while in the positive discharge machines the buckets are completely inverted at the discharge point. The buckets are transported either by a belt or chain. In the centrifugal discharge machines the use of the belt is more usual while the positive discharge units favour the chain, or possibly twin chains on the larger units.

Pneumatic elevator This type of unit is extremely popular in DOCKS for the unloading of ocean-going ships into lighters or shore installations at rates as high as 2000 tons per hour. The grain is drawn up through hoses by suction created by a centrifugal fan or rotary blower operating at the discharge end. The operation of the flexible intake hoses on jibs allows this system to effectively overcome the problems of trimming the hold and simultaneously accommodating variations in height due to tidal changes. On a smaller scale, in the region of 70 to 80 tons per hour, similar systems are in operation mounted on trailers and powered by an integral diesel engine. This small unit benefits from its mobility as well as enjoying much the same flexibility as the static unit.

Chain type elevator This consists of a steel tube enclosing a continuous chain which has extensions or 'paddles' on the links to carry the grain along. Machines of this type operate on the *en masse* principle, which is that once the supply of material to the unit is started it is allowed to fill the elevator from inlet to outlet; thus the particles of the material being conveyed propel each other along in conjunction with the chain of the machine. This can be done effectively either horizontally or vertically, or by using a combination of these.

Archimedean screw elevator This type of unit, often referred to as an *auger*, operates on the *en masse* principle and the machine is generally inclined at an angle of 70 to 80° to the horizontal, with a length of approximately 30 ft (9 m). Mounted on a two-wheeled chassis and with capacities of 20 to 30 tons per hour, machines of this style are in common use in the agricultural industry.

Vertical screw elevators are an extension of the horizontal Archimedean screw conveyer principle and operate on an *en masse* basis, but by a series of variations of the pitch and diameter of the blades they can carry material at a predetermined loading vertically up the machine.

Below left: the hose of a pneumatic elevator unloading grain from the hold of a ship. Static elevator installations may be part of a silo complex, discharging the grain straight into the bins. The mobile elevator units discharge into mills or silos, or directly into road vehicles or rail trucks.

Below right: a dockside pneumatic elevator in Argentina.

Bottom right: a conveyer belt elevator suitable for use on farms.

DIAGRAM VISUAL INFORMATION LTD

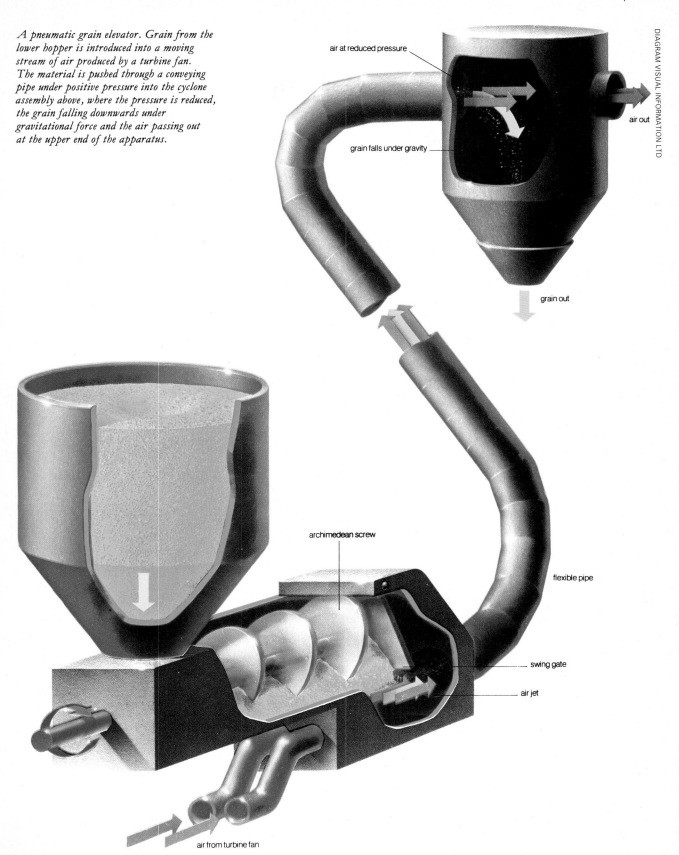

A pneumatic grain elevator. Grain from the lower hopper is introduced into a moving stream of air produced by a turbine fan. The material is pushed through a conveying pipe under positive pressure into the cyclone assembly above, where the pressure is reduced, the grain falling downwards under gravitational force and the air passing out at the upper end of the apparatus.

air at reduced pressure

air out

grain falls under gravity

grain out

archimedean screw

flexible pipe

swing gate

air jet

air from turbine fan

EMBOSSING MACHINES

When a raised pattern is produced on a surface it is said to be embossed. This is one of the oldest methods of decorating metal. When a thin sheet of metal is decorated by beating it up from the underside, a technique widely used for making jewellery, it is called *repoussé*. This is embossing by hand, but for most applications a die and a counterdie are used.

The design or pattern is drawn or inscribed on the face of the die; then the surface is machined away around the pattern so that it is left raised. The counterdie is engraved to match the die, so that when a thin strip of metal or plastic between them and the die is forced into the counterdie the pattern is impressed or embossed upon it. Die stamping has been used for many years for the manufacture of metal parts; for embossing on relatively light materials the principle is the same.

Die stamping is a method of producing distinctive personalized stationery and letterheads, in which the paper is pressed between the dies and the ink applied to the top surface at the same time. Printers nowadays are offering this service less often because the same thing can be accomplished more cheaply without the use of dies, which are expensive to make. In the new method, thermographic powder sticks to a normal inked design and expands on the application of heat.

The most common example of embossing today is the method of producing labels or nameplates. Large machines which embossed strips of aluminium used to be common on railway station platforms. In the United States, bus stations and amusement parks still have machines which emboss letters and numbers around the perimeter of a coin-shaped trinket. The operator deposits a coin in the machine, dials the chosen character and pulls a lever for each character, up to about 25

being permitted. The British machine which used the aluminium strip dispensed a strip to any desired length at a penny for ten characters. These types of machines use the die and counterdie method of impressing relatively soft metals.

The last dozen years or so have seen the widespread popularity of small hand-operated embossing machines used for making labels. The letters and numbers are embossed on a strip of soft metal or, more commonly vinyl tape. Vinyl has a particular quality that has not been entirely explained—when it is stressed the colouring material is forced away from the stressed section leaving it an opaque white. This property is exploited to produce easily legible embossed tapes by using coloured tapes that contrast strongly with the white of the stressed area. The tapes are backed with a pressure sensitive adhesive coating, allowing them to be applied to almost any surface. A wide range of metal tapes are also available for these portable machines for different temperatures and corrosive environments, but these rely purely on the embossing for legibility—there is no contrast between the characters and the background as there is with the vinyl tapes.

The actual embossing machines used with these tapes are quite simple, consisting of a wheel in two parts with the alpha-

Below: a typical small embossing device for general home and office use. A plastic tape with a protected adhesive backing is inserted between the two discs. These revolve so that the tape rests between the dies of a chosen letter. When the hinged handle is pressed the discs are forced together, leaving a white impression on the plastic. A ratchet wheel moves the tape on for the next letter. Spaces between letters are made by depressing the lever only halfway, working the ratchet but not pressing the dies home.

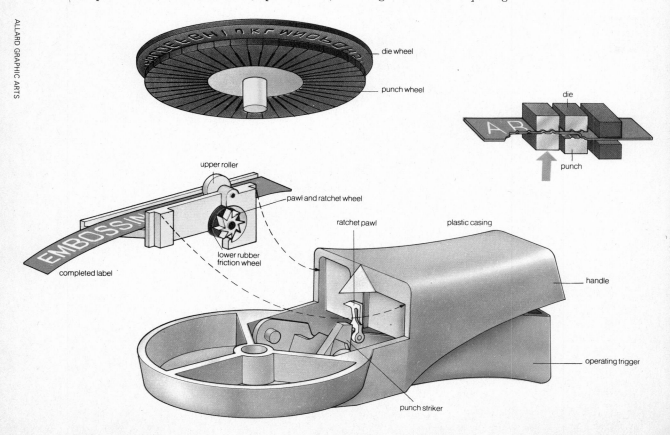

die wheel

punch wheel

die

punch

upper roller

pawl and ratchet wheel

ratchet pawl

plastic casing

lower rubber friction wheel

completed label

handle

operating trigger

punch striker

numeric characters on it. The wheel is in two parts, fixed to rotate together. The top section has the characters engraved in depth and is rigid. The bottom section is made of a different plastic and the characters are separated at the periphery although joined at the centre so that each character can be pressed into the corresponding counterdie on the upper portion of the wheel. The tape is fed into the machine and the wheel turned to the required letter or number. The lever is depressed and the character embossed on the tape which is automatically moved forward by a small ratchet mechanism. A tiny blade is incorporated in the top section of the wheel to cut off the tape when the message is finished. The initial movement of the handle or lever causes the tape to advance, so the tape can be moved without embossing if wished. On the simpler machines it is important to pull the lever firmly in order to make a good impression as it is dependent solely on hand pressure.

Below left: a metal embossing press. The male die is installed on the bed of the press and the plate to be embossed, which in this case is already colour printed, is placed over it. Then the press operates to bring the female die down on top of it. One operator removes the embossed plate and the other places a fresh one in the press.

Below right: female (left) and male dies.

Lower left: a typical use of the embossing machine, a snuff-box lid. The lid forming operation is usually done by the press at the same time as the embossing.

Lower right: a machine for embossing plastic plates, such as credit cards. Operated by magnetic tape, it can make 10,000 cards a day.

ENAMELLING

In enamelling a thin layer of glass is fused to the surface of a metal. Being a glass, enamel has a hard glossy surface which is resistant to corrosion, scratching and staining. Because of these properties it is used extensively for household goods such as stoves, washing machines, refrigerators, baths and smaller items such as pots, pans, plates and mugs. Roadsigns are also often enamelled. The term enamel (more correctly vitreous or porcelain enamel) should not be confused with the use of this word as applied to high gloss paints.

The technique of enamelling to create jewellery and pictures has its origins in antiquity and was known to the early Egyptians, the Celts, and the Romans, and developed even more by the Byzantines. Recently there has been a widespread revival of the craft of enamelling.

Industrial enamelling was first developed commercially in the 1850s in Austria and Germany with the enamelling of sheet steel. During the later half of the nineteenth century mass produced enamel goods became available, and twentieth century technology has continued to improve the quality.

Preparation of powdered glass In large scale industrial applications a continuous smelter is used. The well mixed raw materials are fed in at one end and the molten glass flows out at the other. It is then cooled by pouring into cold water or on to a cooled metal surface. This glass, called *frit*, is easily ground to small particles in a ball mill. For sheet steel enamelling the frit is milled with clay, certain electrolytes (see ELECTROLYSIS) and water to provide a stable suspension or slurry. Particle size varies, a *ground* or base coat enamel being about 0.07 mm, while *cover* coats are finer, probably less than 0.04 mm in diameter.

The chemical composition of the glass varies according to the job it must do, but it is important that the rates of expansion on heating and contraction on cooling are compatible with those of the metal to be enamelled. A typical ground coat, which is the first coat to be applied in sheet steel enamelling, might contain 39 to 42% borax, felspar 19 to 21%, silica 28 to 30%, sodium carbonate 7 to 9% and small amounts of other chemicals including cobalt or sometimes molybdenum oxides to help the enamel to adhere well to the metal. The next layer of enamel is the cover coat (more than one may be applied) and it may contain 23 to 26% borax, 13 to 15% felspar, 33 to 36% silica, 9 to 13% sodium carbonate and various other chemicals, including 5 to 7% titanium oxide. Titanium oxide is added for opacity and other opaque materials also used include zirconia, antimony oxide and molybdenum oxide. In fact titanium enamels have excellent covering power. For example, one thin coating about three thousandths of an inch thick will mask a dark coloured ground coat.

The enamelling process

It is most important that the metal surface is clean before the frit is applied and, indeed, the surface should be clean for all subsequent enamel coats. The most common industrial metals are steels (including a very low carbon enamelling steel for one-coat white enamelling) enamelling iron and sometimes cast iron. The sheet metal articles are thoroughly cleaned in a series of baths including detergent, acid, alkali and water for thorough rinsing. To enhance enamel bonding, sometimes a thin film of nickel is plated on.

Most enamelling is done by the wet process; a thick slurry of the frit is applied by spraying or dipping followed by draining. The dry process is used for cast iron enamelling. Here the first coat is applied wet but the subsequent cover coats are applied by dusting the powdered glass on to the heated article; several dusting and heating cycles are needed for uniformity.

After drying, the enamel is fired either in intermittent box type furnaces or in a continuous tunnel type furnace. In the latter case the articles travel slowly through the furnace on a conveyer, the journey taking about 20 minutes, but they only remain in the hot part of the furnace for about four minutes. Ground coats are normally fired at about 800 to 850 °C (1470 to 1560 °F), while cover coats are fired for shorter times at a slightly lower temperature.

On heating, the glass melts and draws up with surface tension to the metal. It is not known exactly why it bonds so well but probably it is a combination of physically gripping the 'rough' metal surface (no matter how smooth a metal may appear it is actually full of minute hills and valleys), and the formation of chemical bonds between the glass and metal.

Jewellery and craft enamelling

In many ways the procedures are similar to industrial enamelling, but often on an

To prepare vitreous enamel frit, the raw materials are thoroughly mixed and fed into a furnace at a temperature of 1300 °C (2360 °F). The molten glass is poured into water to quench it.

After being coated with enamel slurry, baths travel on an overhead conveyer through a furnace at a temperature of about 850 °C (1560 °F), and are fired for about 5 minutes to fuse the enamel.

individual scale. The glass formulae differ—a typical craft enamel consisting of 33% silica, 33% red lead, 9% borax, 12% sodium carbonate, 7% potassium nitrate and small percentages of other chemicals. Metallic oxides may be added to the frit as colouring agents, up to 15%. There are three basic types of enamel: transparent, translucent and opaque.

The metals used most frequently are copper or copper alloys, but silver, gold, platinum and stainless steel may also be enamelled. The frit is usually applied by dusting it evenly on to the metal surface, which has previously been coated with an adhesive, usually gum tragacanth, to make the powdered glass stick. Alternatively the frit may be slurried. There are various design effects in craft enamelling: cloisonné, champlevé, and basse taille. In cloisonné the metal surface is divided into individual 'cells' by thin strips of metal which have been soldered or fixed in a colourless flux (glass) to the surface. These cells can then be filled with different coloured enamels without any fear of mixing. The art of cloisonné was developed during the Byzantine period, the cells originally being made of thin gold strips fixed to a gold base. Although it was known to the Romans, champlevé was not widely used until the twelfth century. Cavities are scooped out of the metal to hold the enamel. In basse taille the metal surface is designed in low relief and then covered all over with transparent enamel, so that the design beneath shows through the enamel.

Baths, enamelled with a tough white cover coat, emerge from the furnace. Most white enamels contain titanium oxide. After undergoing inspection the baths are protected and stacked.

Top: an early example of 9th century Byzantine cloisonné work— the Hope Beresford Cross, which depicts the Crucifixion. The individual cells for the various coloured enamels were formed from thin gold strips. The best Byzantine cloisonné work is 11th century.

Bottom: unlike glass or pottery, the firing of enamel takes only a few minutes. Here a dish is carefully placed in the muffle furnace.

ENERGY

Energy is *work* in its broadest scientific sense. A bullet in motion possesses energy by virtue of its motion and this energy (called *kinetic energy*) is 'given up' or transferred on hitting a target. The energy of the bullet goes into deforming or breaking the target, that is, doing work on the target, and as heat and sound. A bullet at rest does not possess this energy.

A mass raised against gravitational force possesses *potential energy* because it has a 'potential' to move by virtue of its position. If allowed to fall to the ground this mass can do work, that is, its potential energy can be used to do something, such as hammer a pile into the ground to support the foundations of a building.

Kinetic and potential energy are both forms of stored energy relating to the motion of bodies or their potential to move (see DYNAMICS) and as such form the basis of mechanical physics.

There are, however, many other forms in which energy exists.

A drum of oil is inert when left to itself, yet it contains latent (undeveloped) chemical energy which can be used in a DIESEL ENGINE, for example, to drive a train. The thrust developed by burning liquid fuel in a rocket can impart the energy needed to launch a space vehicle.

Energy is stored in the magnetic field of a permanent magnet because it will move a piece of iron in the vicinity—thus doing work on the iron. Also, energy can be transferred from place to place in the form of radiation. This can be heat radiation or light, in fact, any form of ELECTROMAGNETIC RADIATION. It is in this form that the Earth receives energy from the Sun.

Energy is convertible from one form to another—in some cases with ease, as in the pendulum which interchanges potential and kinetic energy during its cyclical swinging. In other situations, man-made energy conversion devices are required. In an

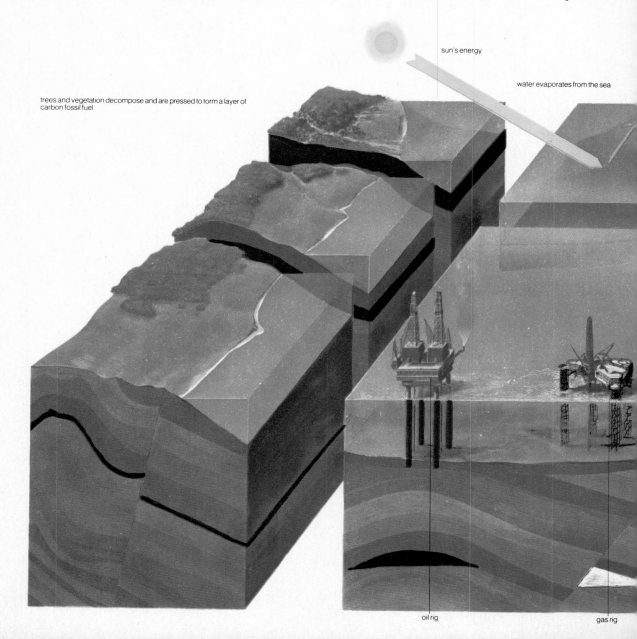

DIAGRAM VISUAL INFORMATION LTD

sun's energy

water evaporates from the sea

trees and vegetation decompose and are pressed to form a layer of carbon fossil fuel

oil rig

gas rig

electrical generating station, for example, the chemical energy of coal or oil is released by combustion as heat to raise steam, converted into rotary energy in a turbine, then again converted into electrical energy in an electromagnetic generator (DYNAMO or ALTERNATOR).

Such conversions are never fully effective. For example, in a power station only about 40% of the latent energy of the fuel is converted into electricity. But if the energy 'lost'—which

Below : a landscape illustrating some of the main forms of natural energy. Heat from the sun's rays evaporates water from the surface of the sea forming clouds which are later precipitated as rain over the hills. This water can then be used to generate hydroelectricity. Other forms of energy derive from fossil fuel formed over millions of years from compressed and decomposed vegetation. Nuclear power is generated using naturally radioactive substances.

eventually becomes low grade heat—is accounted for in the energy balance-sheet, the total quantity of energy sums to the same amount on both sides. This is a statement of the principle of energy conservation—one of the CONSERVATION laws in physics.

The nature of energy It is impossible to say what energy is because energy, like time, is a concept so basic that there are no terms available more fundamental to describe it. It can only be quantified in more basic units (see DIMENSIONS), for example, by relating it to mass, velocity, temperature and so on. Yet although the concept is the cornerstone of modern scientific thinking, it is little more than a century old.

Sir Isaac Newton, in formulating his epoch-making laws of motion, did not mention energy. The term (from the Greek word meaning work) was coined by Thomas Young (1773–1829) eighty years after Newton and applied to what is now

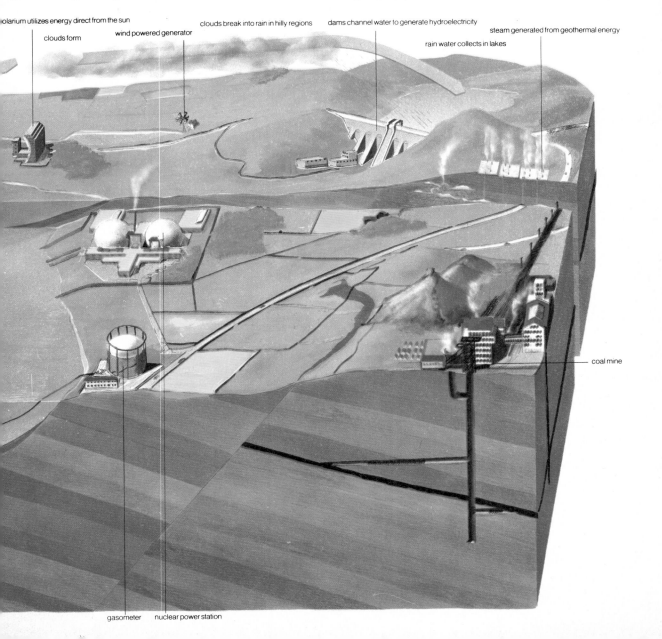

solarium utilizes energy direct from the sun

clouds form

wind powered generator

clouds break into rain in hilly regions

dams channel water to generate hydroelectricity

rain water collects in lakes

steam generated from geothermal energy

coal mine

gasometer   nuclear power station

called the kinetic energy of a body. A body of mass m moving with velocity v has a kinetic energy of $\frac{1}{2}mv^2$. Half a century later, Rankine coined the term potential energy.

Both these terms concern mechanical physics, and their relation to thermal energy (HEAT) was not realized until Joule (1818–1889) demonstrated two crucial experiments. He showed that the heat produced by the passage of an electric current through a wire was related to the square of the current and also that heat was produced by mechanical work. In 1847 he obtained the mechanical equivalent of heat by measuring the temperature rise in water resulting from the action of a paddle driven by a falling mass. This experiment convinced Lord Kelvin (1824–1907), although CARNOT (1796–1832), father of the HEAT ENGINE, never accepted that heat was other than a 'fluid', called caloric, possessed by 'hot' bodies. After Joule, the principle of energy convertibility gained rapid ground and with it the concept of energy conservation.

Energy and mass
Until Einstein (1879–1955) enunciated his theory of relativity, the energy conservation concept remained unassailed. Along with this grew the idea of the conservation of mass which states that matter can be rearranged but not destroyed.

Einstein's theory modified both of these fundamental concepts. He showed that every physical occurrence, of whatever kind, can be specified completely only if it is known when as well as where it occurred. A physical 'event' is placed not only in the three dimensions of space but also in the fourth dimension of time. A body in motion therefore exists in such a system and its velocity relative to a (stationary) observer is important in determining the properties of that body. There is a limiting factor here, however, as nobody can travel faster than the speed of light (usually denoted c) and as a body approaches this speed both its observed mass and energy tend to become infinitely large. This led Einstein to the conclusion that a mass m at rest is equivalent to an amount of energy given by $m \times c^2$, but in motion the effective mass (and therefore the effective energy) increases according to the velocity v of the body in relation to the velocity of light c.

The equivalence of mass and energy has been triumphantly verified. It elucidates the phenomena of RADIOACTIVITY, the explosion of the A-BOMB and the production of energy by nuclear FISSION. Where such a reaction takes place an enormous amount of energy is released accompanied by a reduction (which is actual) in total mass. Thus the production of vast quantities of radiant energy emitted by the stars is the result of a conversion of a small fraction of their mass into radiation.

Terrestrial energy
Although energy is indestructible there is a tendency in nature for it to become unusable. To be usable, that is, to do work, it must be able to 'flow'—to be transferred from place to place. Energy becomes unusable when this transfer is no longer possible.

All hot bodies become colder and cold bodies become warmer and so gradually a common temperature is reached.

Below: a solar prominence. The sun, like all stars, produces enormous quantities of energy from the conversion of a relatively small amount of matter. This energy leads to a constant turmoil in the star's structure, shown by this gas plasma flare from its surface.

PHOTRI

A heat engine will only function with a usable temperature difference because only then can heat energy flow. Eventually, it would seem, the whole energy content of the universe will become low-grade heat and we shall be left with no means of using it.

When the earth was formed it was endowed with a vast store or energy—the potential energy of its atoms, its internal heat energy and its kinetic energy of rotation. Since creation, moreover, it has been receiving energy from the sun, part of which was stored in the distant past as coal, oil and natural gas, more recently as peat, wood and vegetation. The capital resources, stored in prehistory, can be drawn upon until they are used up and become low-grade heat; while current resources depend almost entirely on the sun, and even if they could be exploited to the full they would not meet the present world demand.

Units of energy The historic growth, side by side, of branches of physics, between which any interrelation remained unsuspected, led to many different scientific and legal units in which energy can be specified. Examples are calories, therms and British thermal units (for heat), watt-hours (for electrical energy), foot-pounds and kilogram-metres (for mechanical energy), gauss-oersteds (for the permanent magnet industry) and several others. The modern view of the unit of energy, together with the awkward numerical conversion factors otherwise necessary, led to the adoption of a single basic unit. This is the joule, named after the scientific amateur from Manchester who demonstrated energy equivalence in the middle of the 19th century.

ENERGY SOURCES

Man's use of energy has steadily grown during his existence on Earth, from the fires of his primitive ancestors to the modern very intensive use in the developed world. Only recently has there been any suggestion that the amount of energy available may not be enough to meet all the requirements. These arise mainly out of the industrial nations' various huge needs, which have not been pre-planned but have rather arisen independently of each other. A change in social attitudes, maybe forced by lack of energy, could alter these requirements, just as the discovery of new oil reserves can change the picture as well. It is therefore possible only to give estimates of energy sources and demands, which could turn out to be quite wrong. This article therefore gives current estimates which assume that energy use will carry on in its present form.

One school of opinion believes that it would be preferable to make better use of energy (see CONSERVATION TECHNOLOGY) by, for example, insulating homes, using SOLAR ENERGY to run them, growing food at home rather than using an agricultural system which requires vast inputs of mechanized energy, and increased use of electronic communications to avoid the need for travel. These imply a considerable change in attitudes and social life.

Nuclear-power stations such as this one may help solve the energy crisis. But all fission-processes produce radioactive waste which must be kept isolated for hundreds of years. Disposing of the waste in space is one suggestion, but the risk of a catastrophic launch accident may make this method too potentially dangerous to use.

Energy requirements The units of energy are joules, or in a more familiar unit, calories. The energy in food is usually quoted in kilocalories, or Calories. Power stations, however, are usually rated in power units, watts, which do not take into account the time over which the power is used. Energy sources can therefore be quoted in a variety of units, but here the basic power unit of watts (and the multiples kilowatts, kW, and megawatts, MW) will be used.

Humans need only 0.15 kW per man as food for light effort (1 kW = 239 calories/second), but European man used a total of 5 kW per man in 1970, both for food and for other uses, to provide the material standard of life to which he is accustomed. In the underdeveloped countries the figure was about 0.5 kW, while in the USA it was 10 kW. About a quarter of the energy consumption of a developed country is used for room heating and household appliances, a quarter for transport,

Two ways of using solar power. Above left are solar cells, as used to power spacecraft. Although experimental devices have efficiencies as high as 18%, a more common figure is 12%. Thus one square metre of cells facing the sun would have about 1.3 kW of energy shining on it, of which only 150 W would appear as electricity. Another way is to use solar heat directly, as in Australia (below). This distils brackish water, collecting the fresh evaporated water on the glass plates. Alternatively, by focusing the sun's heat to produce steam, electricity can be generated at an overall efficiency of 30%.

and the remainder for industrial and agricultural production.

So far most of the energy has been obtained from the combustion of fossil fuel—coal, oil and natural gas. In the developed countries, the fraction of the energy which is used to produce electricity was about $\frac{1}{4}$ in 1970 and will probably rise to $\frac{1}{3}$ by 1980. The upshot is that by 1980 the world will require energy at the rate of about 13×10^6 MW, of which 4×10^6 MW will be used for the production of electricity. If the whole world were to be brought up to US levels of consumption these figures would need to be multiplied by six. (1 MW of power = 1340 horse power; and 1 MW yr of energy is equivalent to one thousand 1 kW fires operating for one year.)

The oil reserves may seem large (430×10^6 MW yr) until the cumulative oil consumption is taken into account: in fact they would be exhausted around the year 2020 even if the annual increase in consumption dropped to 5% from 1980 onwards, and even if progress is made in developing economic methods of extracting oil from tar sands and oil shales. In contrast with oil, coal reserves are large; but they will be needed for the production of plastics and oil as well as power. Provided that coal is not used for many more decades as fuel in electricity generating stations (which at present waste at least 60% of the energy), it will be a useful source of hydrocarbons for the chemical industry for another century.

Fossil fuels represent the accumulation of 400 million years of solar energy transformed by *photosynthesis* in plants. On any reasonable time scale they must be regarded as non-renewable resources, and the end of man's brief fossil fuel period of 2000 years is in sight. What are the alternatives?

Water power Evaporation by the sun and rainfall on high ground represents the largest renewable concentration of solar energy. (Wind power is vast, but too widely distributed to be useful except on a small scale—see WINDMILL and WIND POWER). The power of water is harnessed by allowing it to fall under gravity through TURBINES which drive electric generators, and consequently this source of energy is referred to as *hydroelectric power*. The potential world capacity of hydroelectric power is about 2.9×10^6 MW but only 7% is being used. Unfortunately many of the unused sources are far from centres of population and industry, and transmission costs, which are very high, cannot be ignored. Furthermore, such schemes may affect the environment, for example by altering the flow of rivers and causing silting up. Therefore, although useful for many underdeveloped regions, hydroelectric schemes can be no answer to the needs of the developed world.

Tidal power The total worldwide potential power of the tides is 3×10^6 MW. But the power available from usable

The blue glow of Cerenkov radiation, produced when fast electrons enter water, is a sign of the vast energy production rate of a nuclear reactor. This demands rapid energy extraction, raising doubts about what would happen should the extraction systems fail.

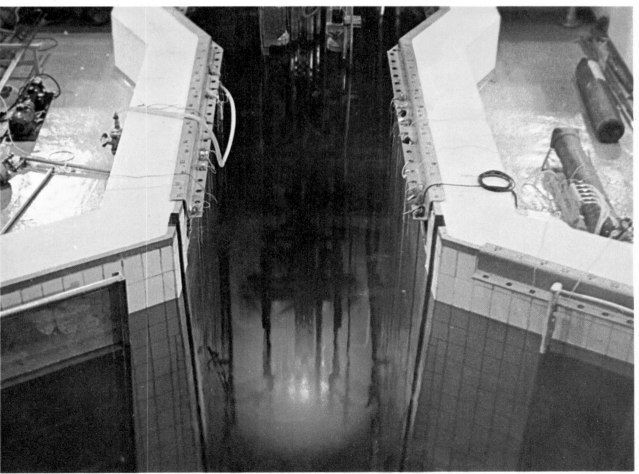

shallow seas and estuaries having tidal ranges of more than 10 feet (3 m) is merely 64,000 MW, and the actual electrical output would be even less. The only TIDAL BARRAGE in operation is that on the river Rance in France, producing electricity at an average power of 100 MW—compared with a large power station's 1000 MW. Tidal power can make only a minor contribution to world requirements, mainly by improving the overall efficiency of a regional electricity supply in conjunction with pumped storage systems (see ENERGY STORAGE).

Geothermal power   Steam is available from hot springs in volcanic regions and the total installed generating capacity is about 1200 MW. Assuming that about 1% of the potential energy available can be tapped, and converted to electricity with an efficiency of 25%, the potential yield is estimated to be 3×10^6 MW yr. If withdrawn over a 50 year period, this source would provide about 60,000 MW of power. Highly significant though it is to a country like Iceland which has no fossil fuel, this source is irrelevant in global terms.

The heat energy in these volcanic regions is thought to arise from a near-surface concentration of a more widely dispersed heat source of radioactively decaying material about 20 miles (30 km) below the surface. Deep drilling projects might lead to this source of *geothermal heat* being tapped in regions where the hot rock is not too deep, although the power required to pump a heat transfer fluid through fissured rock would be considerable. The heat available from liquid granite magma at 900 °C, as it cools and crystallizes at 500 °C, is about 60,000 MW per cubic kilometre. At 20% conversion efficiency, which is optimistic, a cubic kilometre of magma could support a 1000 MW station for only 12 years. Geothermal energy is unlikely to be the answer to the energy crisis.

Solar radiation   About 30% of the sun's radiation is reflected by the earth's atmosphere, 20% is absorbed by it, and 50% reaches the earth's surface. In favourable regions the average intensity at the surface is 240 MW per square kilometre. This is certainly a valuable and under-used resource, but is it a feasible alternative to fossil fuel for electricity generation? With present technology, less than 15% of the solar power falling on an area can be converted to electricity, so a 1000 MW plant, equivalent to a large power station, would need a

The Earth's internal heat appears at the surface as steam in a few parts of the world. This is a view of a geothermal power station at Taupo, New Zealand: the steam is tapped and fed directly to turbines, after which the electricity production stage is the same as in almost any other power station.

COLORIFIC

collector surface area of more than 16 square miles (42 km²).

An alternative involves collecting the solar power by satellite in space, where the intensity is a constant 1390 MW/km². The energy would be beamed as microwave power to collectors on earth. These would cover a large area—some 3 square miles (8 km²) for the 1000 MW plant—but would consist of wire arrays which would not prevent the use of land beneath them. Although initial costs would be high, because a space shuttle programme would be required, the scheme would be non-polluting with an inexhaustible fuel supply.

Nuclear energy

NUCLEAR REACTORS use radioactive fuel to produce heat by FISSION which is then used to make electricity in a more or less conventional way. The initial fuel, uranium 235, is in short supply, but breeder reactors which are being developed actually produce more fissile material than they use.

It may thus appear that nuclear fission is the answer, but a major drawback is the amount of radioactive waste produced. This takes several hundred years to decay to a safe level, and is being produced in increasing amounts. At present it can only be stored. The safe transport of fuel elements between reactors and fuel processing plant is another serious problem.

FUSION, the other means of producing nuclear energy, would be much safer, using deuterium (from sea water) and tritium (from lithium, which is plentiful). So far, however, no practical methods of controlling fusion reactions have been developed.

Vegetation as a power source

The world's annual forest woody increment is estimated to be $12,900 \times 10^6$ tons of which only 13% is harvested. The remaining 87% is capable of producing 5×10^6 MW yr, a quantity approaching the present annual world power consumption. Unfortunately, this source, like the wind, suffers from lack of concentration. The ecological and climatic effects of indiscriminate cutting would be severe but, given scientific management on a continuous basis, forests could be a useful source of power for some underdeveloped countries.

The production of photosynthesized material as an energy source on a minor scale might be possible using streams and ponds loaded with organic effluent. These can produce material at a rate comparable with that of good arable land, about 10 times the rate of production in forests. Certainly arable land itself cannot be used for power production: it will all be needed

A river provides a useful source of power, but the energy available depends on the 'head' or distance through which the water can fall. For this reason, hydroelectric power schemes are usually confined to hilly regions, as is this one at Sogsvirkjun, Iceland

MATS WIBE LUND

for agriculture. The world population is expected to increase to about 6×10^9 by the year 2000, and the energy required for food production will then be about 1×10^6 MW. If the energy problem is not solved, it could mean a drop in material standards in the developed countries, or famine in the underdeveloped. This survey has shown that water power, geothermal sources, and terrestrial solar radiation (whether via solar collectors or photosynthesis) can make only a minor contribution. The two safe, long-lived, sources of power, namely fusion and space solar energy, are not yet within our grasp.

The problem involved in meeting the world's energy requirements are not all technical—just as complex are the social and political aspects. There are, however, many known ways of increasing the efficiency with which we use our energy resources. One estimate of the global saving that could be made is 4% of the estimated consumption by 1980 and 9% by 1990. The 1980 saving is equivalent to 225 nuclear reactors each of 1000 MW electrical output. In this way a reasonable annual increase in demand could be met without a large expansion of fission power, with its attendant radioactive waste problems, and without depleting our resources of fossil hydrocarbons.

Using the wind as an energy source demands numbers of windmills. These are multiblade windpumps, with a limited speed. By using fewer blades, as in a propeller, much higher speeds can be reached and the power generated in a strong wind could be about 1 kW per mill.

ZEFA

ENERGY STORAGE

Man can never create or destroy energy, a result of the natural CONSERVATION LAWS, but he frequently converts energy from one form to another by a process which produces a result he desires. Apart from solar and nuclear energy, the original source of energy is invariably some natural form in which energy was stored (see ENERGY SOURCES) and storage of the original resource, such as carrying fuel in the tank of a vehicle, is one form of storage very widely used. There are, however, a number of cases where, having released the energy from its natural storage, it is advantageous to store it again for later recovery, even if this involves a further conversion process and loss of some of the potential for doing useful work.

The reasons for such storage are: to even out fluctuations in demand; to store energy which might otherwise be wasted so that it can be used later; to accumulate energy over a long period for release very rapidly; and to convey energy to where it is required when continuous transmission systems are not practical.

Pumped storage systems

The only large scale method of storing energy which has been developed to operate with the main electrical supply system is known as *pumped storage*. A large electrical machine which can be used either as a motor or a generator is connected to a water turbine and a water pump. This combination of machines is positioned close to a large water reservoir and connected by a series of pipes to a second reservoir placed at a much higher level. The *head* (difference in level) may vary from 100 ft to 2000 ft (30 metres to 700 metres) or occasionally even more. Such arrangements are normally found in mountainous country. During the night when there is plenty of electrical generating capacity available elsewhere which it would be uneconomical to shut down, power is brought to the pumped storage station and used to pump water from the lower reservoir to the high reservoir. At times of high demand (the daytime peak load periods) the pump is disconnected and water is allowed to flow back downhill through the turbine, driving the electrical machine as a generator. The flow of water can be very quickly regulated so that the machine will meet almost instantaneously any demand placed on it up to its maximum capacity.

It is normal for this type of system to generate power for a total of four or five hours each day and to pump up the corresponding amount of water during a period of about six hours during the night. There are inevitable losses in all the machines concerned and friction losses in the pipes, so the total amount of energy recovered is approximately 70% of that absorbed during the pumping operation.

Compressed air and gas systems

Compressors are frequently used to compress air into large pressure vessels from which the energy can be drawn as demand arises. Such systems are very commonly used to operate large numbers of small PNEUMATIC TOOLS and other equipment in factories. To provide individual electricity driven tools would be very expensive and inefficient in terms of energy consumption. The compressed air system allows high efficiency motor driven compressor systems to be used and also gives a steady electrical power demand even if the individual tools present a fluctuating demand. The overall efficiencies for this sort of system are around 50% but the other advantages outweigh the losses.

Compression of gas is also a method of storing up energy in both pneumatic and hydraulic control and power systems. In these systems the pneumatic or hydraulic power may be used to operate parts of machines, to open and close doors on trains, buses and so on. Pneumatic systems use essentially the same pressure vessel previously described; in hydraulic systems where oil is the working fluid a receiver is provided with a flexible diaphragm separating the oil from a trapped volume of air or gas. As oil is forced into the receiver the diaphragm is pressed back and the air on the other side compressed; when the oil flows out again the energy stored in the air is recovered.

Compressed air has been proposed as an alternative to pumped storage schemes. Such systems would use either specially constructed air receivers (probably reinforced concrete structures like some NUCLEAR REACTOR pressure vessels) or the air may be stored underground in natural caverns after suitable sealing. Such schemes have not yet proceeded beyond the design stage.

Electrical storage batteries The most common type of storage battery is the lead-acid ACCUMULATOR which has to be charged up over a period of about 10 hours; when discharged about 90% of the actual current storing capacity (amps x time) is recovered but as the discharge voltage is lower than the charging voltage the actual energy recovered is only about 75% of that used to charge the battery.

For vehicle uses the weight of the battery is particularly important and great efforts have been made to reduce the weight for a given output. Over the last thirty years or so a new class of batteries known as alkali batteries have been developed. These use nickel and cadium or nickel and iron plates in a potassium hydroxide solution. These batteries are very rugged both mechanically and electrically and have found considerable application to ELECTRIC VEHICLE drives, though they are still heavier than the equivalent lead-acid batteries. The current recovery is about 75 to 80% but the energy return is only 60 to 65%.

In 1967, however, the Ford Motor Company announced a completely new type of battery using sodium and sulphur in liquid form separated by solid alumina. The battery has to operate at a temperature of 300 °C but it is claimed to have an output per unit weight of at least six times that of a lead-acid battery. When this type of battery is developed to a suitable stage it should be possible to produce a battery family car with an acceptable performance.

Thermal storage Electrical heating is a very inefficient process as the original generation of electricity involves conversion from fuel to heat, to mechanical power, and then to electrical power with efficiencies of 40% or lower. Conversion of the electrical energy back to heat is clearly wasteful but the

A pumped storage scheme at Ffestiniog, North Wales. The upper reservoir, behind the dam, is 1000 feet (300 m) above the power station at the side of the lower reservoir: it produces 360 MW.

CEGB

overall inefficiency can sometimes be justified on account of cleanliness and convenience. This is particularly so if the efficiency of the overall system can be increased by using power at the low demand periods. Such systems can be used for both domestic and industrial heating by means of storage heater systems.

Electrical resistance wires (similar to those found in an ordinary electric heater) are arranged to pass through a large mass of refractory (heat resisting) material which has a high heat capacity (absorbs a large amount of heat for a comparatively small temperature change). Air passages are provided through the refractory material and the whole assembly is contained in a casing which is thermally insulated so that heat will not be lost to the surroundings. Arrangements are made to allow air to flow through the whole assembly as required and the air then carries away heat to the surrounding space. The flow of air can be controlled by vanes which are generally operated automatically according to the outside temperature. Such systems are normally operated with a time controlled switch

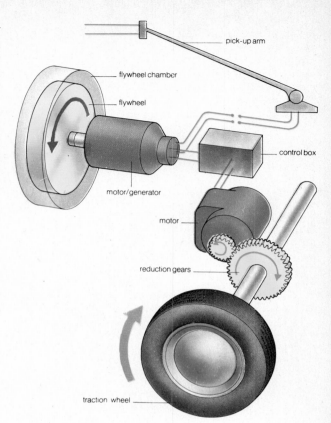

Right: the operating principles of a gyrobus. Power drawn in through the pickup arm drives the motor-generator, which spins the flywheel up to 2950 revs/min. Energy is stored in the flywheel which then drives the motor-generator, producing power for the traction motor.

Below: an electric storage radiator. Coiled elements lie along grooves in the high density fireclay bricks. Low cost electricity supplied at night is used to build up a reservoir of heat in these bricks which can be released later on in the day and circulated round a room by a fan, which draws in air and returns it at a controlled temperature.

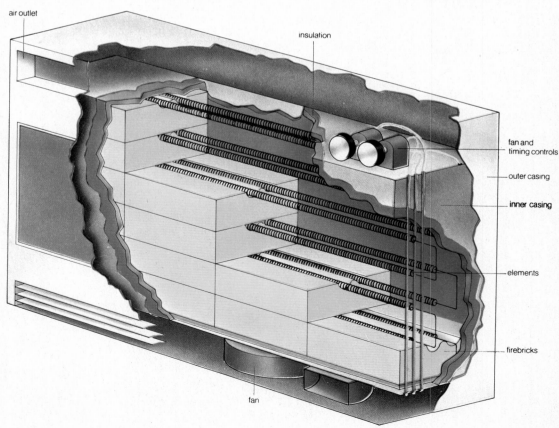

so that heating only takes place during the night but heat may be released at any time. The efficiency of all electric space heating systems is in fact 100% as there is no loss of heat except to the surrounding space where the heat is ultimately required.

Large capacity thermal storage at practically constant temperature can be achieved if, instead of the blocks of refractory material, containers of mixtures of suitable salts are used. The salts are chosen so that the mixture has a melting point at the required temperature. When heat is available for storage, it is absorbed to melt the salts. It can later be released by allowing the salts to resolidify. This type of storage can be used with various types of heat source including solar radiation, but has not yet been used extensively.

Mechanical energy storage
There are a number of systems for storing energy by purely mechanical means though they are rarely used on a large scale. One of the simplest forms is to arrange for railway tracks to slope as they enter and leave each station. In this way the kinetic energy of a train when travelling at speed between stations is converted into potential energy as it climbs the slope (and therefore slows down) when entering the station. On leaving the station it runs down the slope on the other side and potential energy is reconverted to kinetic energy helping the train to accelerate. This system is used on some of the London Tube lines.

There have been many other schemes intended to achieve a similar result (where the road or railway level cannot be controlled) by storing surplus energy in rotation of a flywheel (as kinetic energy) during periods when brakes might otherwise be applied, and recovering the energy when required.

The nearest practical approach to this is the Swiss 'gyrobus'. This does not have a conventional power unit but it gets all the power it requires by plugging into a stationary supply system at each bus stop. Power drawn from the electrical system is used both to accelerate a flywheel and to charge up batteries on the vehicle to meet lighting and other electrical requirements. When the bus is ready to move the supply is disconnected and the electrical machine which drove the flywheel becomes a generator connected to an electric motor driving the wheels with a suitable speed control arrangement. It is possible to store sufficient power in a period of less than two minutes at each stop to allow the bus to travel distances up to about 5 miles (8 kilometres) on level ground and somewhat shorter distances up hills without reducing the total store of energy below the safety level (about half the total energy). A reserve is essential in case the bus is held up for any reason or has to make any detour to pass an obstruction.

Man used a form of strain energy storage for his own purposes for centuries before he had any understanding of the nature of energy. This occurs with bows and arrows, catapults and many other similar devices where the original source of mechanical energy is man's muscle power. This is stored, with 100% efficiency, in the springiness of the wood or the catapult elastic, and then released suddenly.

ENGINE (see individual type)

A view of the Rance tidal project in Brittany, France. This barrage across the river estuary uses its turbines as pumps to assist the tide in filling the estuary. When a sufficient head of water is reached, the water is allowed to flow back through the turbines.

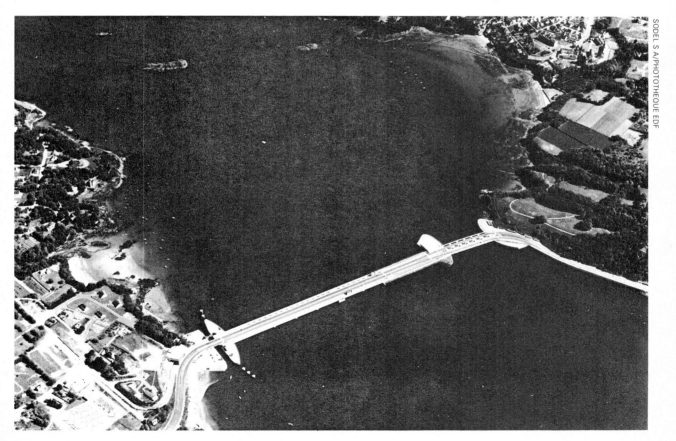

ENGRAVING AND ETCHING

Engraving and etching on metal are old crafts. Although their use as printmaking processes dates only from the fifteenth century, they were in use long before that by metal workers as a means of decorating arms, armour and jewellery by incising a design into the surface of the metal.

In the middle of the fifteenth century the idea of printing from engraved or etched plates occurred at almost the same time in various places in Germany and Italy. In order to keep a record of their original designs, goldsmiths filled the engraved or etched lines in a metal plate with a black greasy mixture and pressed a piece of paper against the plate to pick up the ink from the grooves. Such prints attracted attention due to their unique graphic qualities, different from those of painting or drawing, and capable of reproduction. For centuries, printmaking was taught and practised as a craft; people who could not afford original works of art in their homes could hang prints on their walls, and such prints even constituted education in the days when many people were illiterate.

With the invention of photography, the crafts of engraving and etching as a means of reproduction of pictures died out, but these processes are widely used by artists as media in their own right. The techniques are defined under the general heading of *intaglio* processes. Plates of steel, copper or zinc about two or three millimetres thick (less than ⅛ inch) are used. Grooves, pitted areas and textures are *bitten* into the plate with acid (*etching, aquatint, soft ground*) or directly cut or scratched by the artist using sharp tools (*engraving, drypoint, mezzotint*). To obtain a print from such a plate, ink is pushed into the grooves and the surface of the plate is wiped clean with muslin. The plate is placed on the bed of a copperplate printing press; a sheet of dampened paper is laid on the plate and backed by several layers of fine felt blankets. When taken through the press under pressure, the blankets force the paper into the grooves, where it picks up the ink. Despite all the progress in commercial printing presses, no one has managed to invent a satisfactory automatic process for reproducing works of art from intaglio plates; it is all done by hand.

Engraving   The tool used is called a *burin* or *graver*, and its action is limited to lines and dots. The art of the engraver has been to manipulate this limitation to his advantage, building up a variety of tones and textures by varying the width, depth and size of the lines and dots. An engraving is differentiated from other types of prints by its sharpness and clarity.

The tool is a short, highly tempered steel bar between 2 mm and 5 mm thick (less than ¼ inch), square or lozenge shaped in section. One end is bent up into a mushroom shaped handle, so that when the tool lies flat on the plate the handle comes up comfortably into the palm of the hand. A facet is cut at a 45 to 60° angle on the other end, and the engraving is done with the sharpened tip of the tool by holding it at a shallow angle to the plate and pushing it slowly forward. As the tool cuts grooves in the metal it generates a 'chip' which is removed at the end of the line with the side of the tool. The bigger the angle of the

Below : in line engraving a design is produced by cutting directly into the surface of a copper plate. Etching is a development of this technique in which the design is scored through a coating of wax and then treated with a solution of sulphuric acid which eats away at any exposed copper, leaving the required pattern.

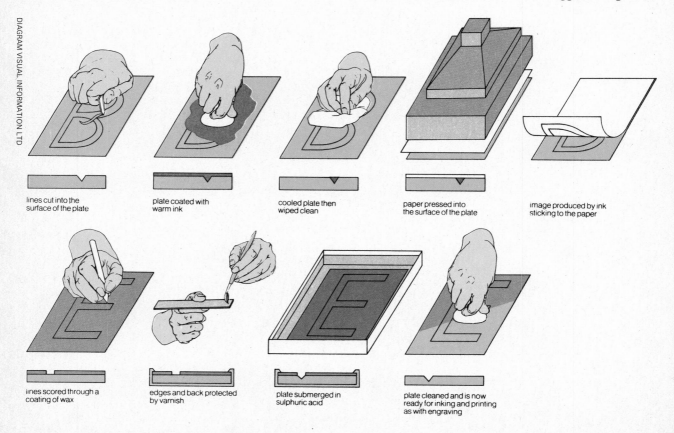

lines cut into the surface of the plate

plate coated with warm ink

cooled plate then wiped clean

paper pressed into the surface of the plate

image produced by ink sticking to the paper

lines scored through a coating of wax

edges and back protected by varnish

plate submerged in sulphuric acid

plate cleaned and is now ready for inking and printing as with engraving tool to the plate, the wider and deeper the incision. The greater the amount of ink which the line will hold, the darker it will print. Curved lines are executed by turning the plate rather than the tool. Round dots are executed by placing the tip of the tool on the plate and turning the plate in a complete circle; it is also possible to execute triangular dots by pushing the tip of the tool into the plate and pulling it out. When the engraving is finished, the plate is polished to remove any burrs at the edges or ends of the incisions.

Drypoint
The drypoint is a similar but distinctly different process. It is done with a tool resembling a pencil sharpened to a fine point, and the line is scratched on to the surface of the plate rather than engraved. Sometimes the tool has a diamond, ruby or sapphire set in the tip, which does not require sharpening. When the line is scratched, a burr is created on either side; it is the burr which will hold the ink and give the soft and feathery printed line which is characteristic of drypoint.

Mezzotint
Mezzotint is a tonal technique, invented in the middle of the seventeenth century and used to copy paintings. It is a time consuming process, requiring elaborate preparation of the plate. The plate is prepared with a tool called a *rocker*, made of hard steel and chisel shaped. The end of the tool is rounded, and has grooves in it from 45 to 120 to the inch; one side of it is sharpened so that the sharp edge is serrated by the grooves. This tool is then rocked across the surface of the plate in as many as eighty different directions until the entire surface of the plate is covered with a texture and no shiny dots of polished surface remain. When the plate is ready, other sharp tools called burnishers and scrapers are used to scrape away the texture to varying depths. The ink held by the plate determines how dark

it will print: the more the texture is scraped away, the lighter that area will print.

Etching
The principle of etching is to protect the surface of the plate with a thin layer of acid-resistant substance called an etching *ground*. The plate is heated and this ground, made of asphaltum, beeswax and resin, is melted on to the surface of the plate and evened out with a roller. When the plate is cooled it is smoked with tapers to harden the ground and to make it evenly black in order to facilitate seeing the drawing. The drawing is scratched through the ground and the plate is bathed in an acid solution. The longer the plate is left in the solution, the deeper the lines, and the darker they will print.

The acids used depend on what type of metal is used. Ferric chloride solutions are used for copper; a carbon steel plate can be etched with a solution of nitric acid and water, mixed 1:4. The amount of water can be varied, depending on how much

Below left: using a burin to engrave a plate. Note the chip curling as the groove is cut. Note also the different textures and types of lines which can be cut on the plate.
Below right: a demonstration of the technique of using a rocker. Note the textured area in front of the tool. The entire surface of the plate must be textured when making a mezzotint; then the textured surface is worked to various depths to make tones.

Bottom left: the artist has painted the plate with ink, and is now wiping it off. The lines made by the engraving tool retain the ink.
Bottom right: the plate has been placed on the press and a piece of paper placed on top of it. Then several thick pieces of felt are piled on and the press forces the paper into the inked grooves.

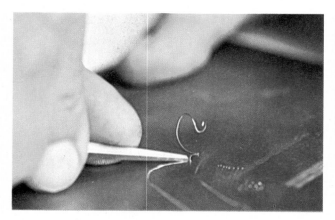

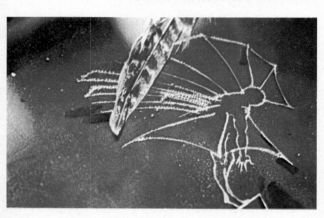

carbon the steel contains and whether it is hard or soft. For brass or nickel plates a mixture of nitric and hydrochloric acid (1:4) can be used.

Aquatint Aquatint is a tonal etching method. It was invented in the eighteenth century in France. The surface of the plate is covered with a thin, even layer of fine powdered resin. The plate is heated from beneath and as the powder melts it forms a uniform surface of acid-resistant granules which firmly adhere to it. The acid will bite into the plate around each granule; the deeper the bite the darker the tone will be. For different tones, the plate is removed from the acid and the lightest tones stopped out with liquid varnish on a brush. This process is repeated until the varying tones are achieved. The resin is washed off the finished etching with methylated spirits.

Sugar aquatint In this technique the drawing is made with a brush using a solution of sugar and India ink. The plate is then coated with diluted acid-resistant varnish which, because it is diluted with turpentine, does not disturb the sugar in the drawing. The plate is then immersed in water; the sugar swells and dissolves, lifting off the varnish in the drawn lines and leaving the image exposed. An aquatint ground is laid and the plate is bitten in the acid.

Soft ground This technique, invented in the eighteenth century, is used to imitate pencil or crayon drawing characteristics. The ground contains grease to keep it from hardening. It is laid on the plate, which is then covered with a sheet of paper. The drawing is done on the paper, and the pressure of the drawing tool causes the ground to stick to the paper when it is removed, exposing the drawing on the plate, which is then bitten in the regular way. Soft ground is also used for taking impressions of fabrics, dried leaves, foil and so on. The material is laid on the plate and covered with paper; it is put through a press with light pressure. When the paper and materials are removed they will have removed the soft ground according to their texture.

Other applications The principles of engraving and etching are used in many applications by science and industry. Bank notes are usually printed by engraved plates to make them hard to counterfeit. Toolmakers use etching and engraving methods to incise trademarks, measurements and other vital data on their products. Metallurgists etch metal samples directly without using a resist (ground) before examining them under microscopes to make their grain characteristics stand out better. Photo engraving (or GRAVURE) processes are used for the reproduction of photographs by a printing press.

ENTHALPY & ENTROPY (see thermodynamics)

Top left: engraving a design on a plate in a silversmith's shop in Jogjakarta, Java, Indonesia.

Second from top: a plate is being prepared for etching by heating it to harden the etching ground. The ground makes a black surface of uniform thickness so that the artist can see the design as he scratches it into the surface.

Third from top: the artist scratches the design into the black ground, using a magnifying glass to check the exact character of the lines. He may use several different scratching tools.

Below left: pushing acid into the lines with a feather.

EPICURUS (341–271 BC)

Epicurus was a Greek philosopher who became the first great thinker of the 'materialist' school (those who seek no further explanation of the universe outside the observable material order of things).

He was a citizen of Athens, and began his teaching career in 311 BC. Hostility to his ideas on the part of traditionalists who regarded them as atheistic forced him to move twice before settling in Athens in 306 BC, where he bought a house and garden in which to establish his school of philosophy, the first, incidentally, to admit women. He ran it less as an institution and more as a community of faithful friends and disciples, where his doctrines were not only learned but put into practice, aiming at moral perfection through spiritual peace and freedom from pain. He died in Athens, and his followers spread his teachings far beyond Greece. Indeed, it is to a later Roman poet, Lucretius (94–55 BC), that we owe most of our knowledge of his theories.

Atomism

Ancient philosophy knew no limits, and its speculations on the nature of the universe ran freely into areas which we would normally classify as scientific. In his youth, Epicurus was influenced by the theories of the atomists, like Democritus (460–357 BC), who denied the older theory that there was one basic substance (infinite and divine) from which all things had their origin. The atomists believed that things had their origin in the actions of ATOMS, countless particles so small that they could not be divided any further. (The Greek word 'atom' actually means 'indivisible'.) This was the theory on which Epicurus based his scientific thought. Collisions between atoms of various size, weight and shape explain the origin of all things. There is no 'creation'; on the contrary, there had always been and would always be two natures: matter, made up of atoms, and space, through which atoms move. Because of their weight, Epicurus believed, all atoms must move in a downward direction, although at an equal velocity. In order to explain how they ever come into contact with each other, since they all move in the same direction, he invented a theory of deflection or swerve in their travel, for which he has been criticized ever since, because there is no scientific justification of this deflection theory.

The universe

There was no limit to the possible number of worlds, according to Epicurus, because the number of atoms was infinite. All that is required for the creation of a world is an atomic storm, out of which a world will evolve. As worlds evolve, so they will also disintegrate in time.

Here again, his real purpose was to show that there is no arbitrary divine purpose in the universe. Everything in it is mortal, because everything is material. He stressed this when he came to consider astronomical and meteorological phenomena, so full of myth and superstition for the ancients. He was prepared to allow that there might be several explanations of the origins of heavenly bodies and their movements; the point was that these explanations could not be anything other than scientific and natural.

Moral theories

The name of Epicurus, however, is chiefly remembered today for his doctrine that happiness and pleasure, together with freedom from fear and from pain, constitute the highest good to which man can aspire. But today's image of the 'epicurean' as one who indulges a cultivated taste for 'the good life' (material comforts) is a gross distortion of the teaching of Epicurus. Although he was a materialist, self control and moderation were central to his philosophy: 'Plain tastes bring us as great a pleasure as the most luxurious diet,' he wrote. Besides excess, the great enemy was fear. In particular, men had to be free not from death but from the fear of death, and from the fear of the imagined anger and punishment of the gods, if they were ever to be happy. (In psychological terms, it may be fear of death which makes men indulge in excess).

The theories of Epicurus taught that the gods lived their own lives and had nothing whatever to do with this world at all: hence it was useless to pray to them or to expect reward or punishment from them. Similarly, although man had a soul, it was a bodily atomic compound with nothing immortal about it at all; it dispersed when the body died, so that man had nothing to fear from threats of what might await him in an afterlife.

Influence

The theories of Epicurus were an anathema in the Christian Middle Ages, and the noble account which he gave of man and the elevated way of life were forgotten amid charges of atheism and hedonism. Only in the seventeenth century at the dawn of the new 'scientific' age was there a revival of interest, particularly in England, in his atomic theories and in his philosophy as a whole among 'mechanistic' philosophers, who were interested in the problem of motion and the explanation of natural phenomena. After an eclipse in the eighteenth century, he was to enjoy new admiration in the nineteenth among materialist thinkers. John Stuart Mill found support for his utilitarian ideas in Epicurus, while Karl Marx wrote his doctoral thesis on Epicurus in 1841.

Below: a bust of Epicurus—the originator of the materialist school of thought. Modern science, which adheres to the same guiding principles, was only developing about 2000 years later.

EPICYCLIC GEARS

The word 'epicycle' is derived from the Greek *epi*, meaning 'upon', and *cyclos*, meaning 'circle'. The epicycle was first used in a model depicting planetary motion, used by Greek astronomers. The epicyclic GEAR system is one in which the centres of one or more gears describe a circle around another gear.

The advantage of an epicyclic gear system is that it provides a number of gear ratios without taking up much space and without requiring gears to be moved in and out of mesh. It is often found in designs for AUTOMATIC TRANSMISSIONS. A gearhub on a BICYCLE is invariably of epicyclic design.

An epicyclic gear system consists of three distinct elements: a *sun* gear, one or more *planet* (or *planetary*) gears mounted on a *planet carrier*, and an *annulus* gear.

The sun gear is mounted on a shaft, and the planet carrier is mounted on another shaft in the same axis. The planet carrier can be visualized as a bracket consisting of one or more arms perpendicular to the shaft, each carrying a pin parallel to the shaft; each pin carries a planet gear which is free to rotate on it. There are usually at least three planet gears to spread out the load, but they are identical, and the number of them has no effect on the system. The planet gears are equidistant from the shaft and from each other; they mesh with the sun gear and run around its perimeter. The annulus gear can best be described as a rim or an outer race with teeth on the inside of its perimeter; it encloses the system, and the planet gears run on the inside of it at the same time as they run around the outside of the sun gear.

Different gear ratios are obtained by driving one element in the system, taking power off a second element, and locking the third so that it cannot turn. For example if the sun gear is driven and the annulus locked, the planet carrier will follow the sun gear at a lower speed in the same direction. If the planet carrier is locked instead, the annulus will turn at the same speed as the sun gear but in the opposite direction. If the planet carrier is driven and the sun gear locked, the annulus will turn at a faster speed in the same direction. Other arrangements are also possible, including locking the whole system so that it transmits drive directly, like a solid shaft.

There are many variations of the epicyclic gear system. A power transmission design may have several epicyclic systems in sequence, or a single epicyclic system may have several sun gears of various sizes, with corresponding sets of planet gears and annulus gears. Each gear element in the system has a different number of teeth, and each can be locked by means of a brake or a clutch to a power driven shaft.

The epicyclic bicycle gear hub is a relatively simple design. In one common design, the gears are selected by means of a square pin which fits into square holes in the gears. The pin is operated by a cable from the gearshift lever. Low gear is provided by locking one of the sun gears, high gear is provided by locking the other, and the middle (or 'normal') gear is provided by locking both. Another design is shown in the diagram. An epicyclic bicycle gear hub may or may not also include a BACK-PEDAL BRAKE. There are also bicycle gear hubs which contain a back-pedal brake and a two-speed gear system which is also operated by back-pedalling; the gearshift is accomplished by back-pedalling a certain distance and back-pedalling further applies the brakes.

Below: one type of 3 speed bicycle hub gear. It has a sliding shaft with two sun gears, and two sets of planet gears mounted on a single planet carrier integral with the chain sprocket; this has a ring of internal teeth that can lock the sun gear to it. A single annulus encloses both planet sets. The annulus drives the bicycle through a freewheel mechanism (not shown). In middle gear, the sun gear shaft is pulled halfway across so that it both meshes with the planet gears and locks into the sprocket. This jams the whole system so that it revolves in one piece with the sprocket. In low gear, the shaft is pulled to the right, so that it locks into the sprocket. It meshes with the left set of planet gears, turning them backwards. They carry the annulus slowly back with them. This, relative to the faster forward movement of the planet carrier, results in the annulus turning forward slowly. In high gear, the sun gear shaft is pulled over to the left so that it is held stationary by a locking clutch, and meshes with the right hand planet wheels. The planet carrier turns around the stationary sun wheel, so that the planet wheels turn forwards. They carry the annulus round with them faster than the sprocket.

Right: a large multiple epicyclic set giving a 400:1 speed reduction.

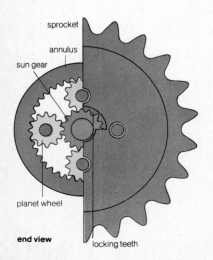

sprocket
annulus
sun gear
planet wheel
end view
locking teeth

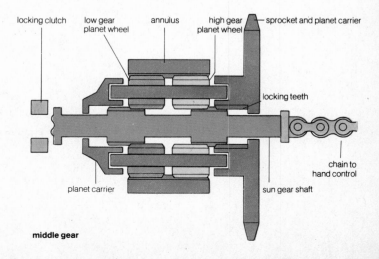

locking clutch — low gear planet wheel — annulus — high gear planet wheel — sprocket and planet carrier
locking teeth
planet carrier
chain to hand control
sun gear shaft
middle gear

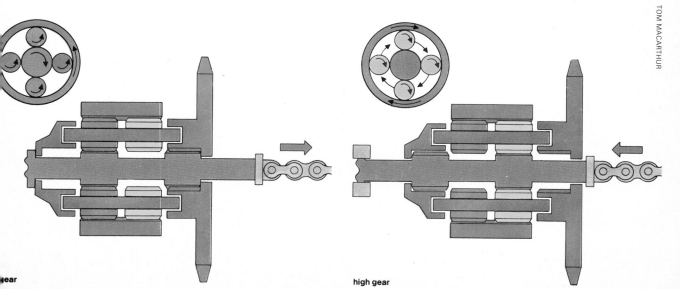

gear

high gear

EQUATORIAL MOUNTING

When astronomers wish to observe stars or other astronomical objects through telescopes, they have to overcome the problem of the Earth's rotation. Except exactly at the Earth's poles and equator, all astronomical objects, including the Sun and Moon, appear to rise at an angle to the horizon, in the east, then move in an arc—a part of a circle—to a high point, finally setting at an angle to the horizon in the west. To follow this motion using a simple mounting would mean that frequent corrections in a stepwise fashion would be necessary. To make matters worse, the orientation of objects changes from rising to setting, as compared to the horizon, so they would appear to rotate slowly in the field of view of the telescope. Although this would not matter for brief observations, the effect would become obvious after more than a few minutes' viewing, and the taking of long exposure photographs would be impossible without further corrections for the field rotation.

These problems are all overcome by using an equatorial mounting. In principle, it consists simply of an axis aligned exactly parallel to that of the Earth's. The telescope is mounted on this *polar* axis on another axis, the *declination* axis, so that it can be pointed at any direction in the sky. The polar axis is then rotated at a precise rate in the opposite direction to the Earth's rotation. This keeps the telescope pointing exactly at one point in space.

The rotation speed used is one turn per 23 hours 56 minutes —the time the Earth takes to rotate with respect to the stars. Because it moves around the Sun as well, the time taken for one point on Earth to turn once with respect to the Sun is four minutes longer, and it is this 24 hour period that we call the day. The Moon appears to move through the sky at a different, and varying, rate. It is therefore common for telescopes to have two drive rates—one for the stars and Sun, and one for the Moon. These will be only approximate in each case, and the final corrections are made using 'slow motion' motors on both telescope axes.

The drive motor may be a simple regulated falling weight, as on many old telescopes; or it may be an ELECTRIC MOTOR synchronized with the frequency of the ALTERNATING CURRENT supply. To vary its speed, the supply frequency is adjusted electronically. A system of gears turns the fairly fast motor speed into the slow movement needed, and for this reason only low power motors are needed. Even the giant 200 inch (5 m) telescope at Mount Palomar, California, has only a 1/12 horsepower (62 watt) motor.

The precise design of the equatorial mounting varies, depending on the size and type of telescope. The ideal requirements are that the telescope should be able to view all parts of the sky, should have its centre of gravity between the bearings of the axes rather than outside them to avoid putting a strain on any part, and should not have to be counterbalanced, which would make the whole thing heavier than necessary. All these requirements are met only in a few very costly mountings.

To align the polar axis with the Earth's, it is set at an angle equal to the telescope's geographical latitude, pointing exactly north-south. The polar axis is then pointing at the pole of the sky—the star Polaris in the northern hemisphere. Graduated circles on each axis will then coincide with the co-ordinate system on which star positions are measured, enabling the telescope to be pointed at any particular star with ease.

EQUILIBRIUM, CHEMICAL (see thermodynamics)

Above: a German type equatorial mounting at Vienna Observatory, often used in the 19th century for refracting telescopes. At the eyepiece, on the left, are controls linked to the right ascension slow motions and clamps, giving the observer full control of the instrument.

Below: the fork mounting is widely used for modern medium sized reflecting telescopes such as this one. The yellow fork rotates on the polar axis, not visible in this picture. Most observing today is photographic or photoelectric, so the telescope is remote controlled.

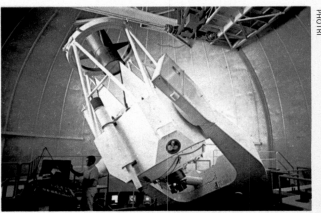

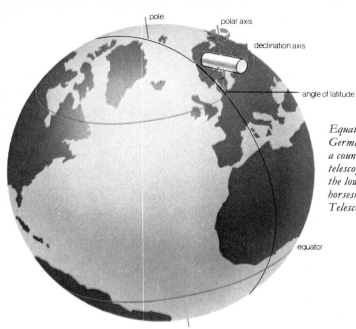

Equatorial mountings have one axis parallel to the Earth's. In the German mounting, the two axes are separate and the telescope needs a counterbalance. The English mounting has no counterbalance, but the telescope cannot observe regions around the Pole Star. The fork is like the lower half of an English mounting and takes up less room. The horseshoe type shown is similar to that of the Anglo Australian Telescope shown in greater detail on page 170 of How It Works.

DIAGRAM VISUAL INFORMATION LTD

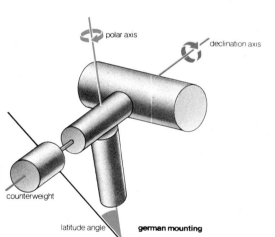

german mounting

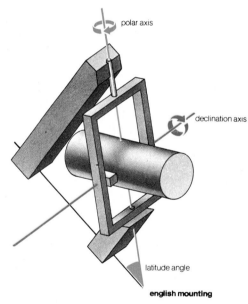

english mounting

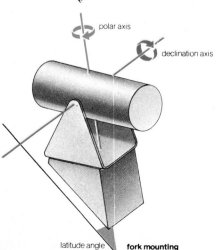

fork mounting

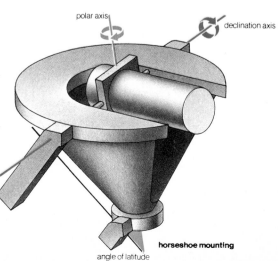

horseshoe mounting

ERGONOMIC DESIGN

Ergonomic design is the attempt to design consumer goods, industrial processes and architectural space so that these things can be used with a minimum of stress. Its attitude is that the human factor should be taken into consideration.

Centuries ago, when human beings built their own homes and made their own tools, they did these things the way their forefathers had done them, and over the centuries the design of everyday objects had evolved to the most useful and pleasant shapes. Objects such as furniture, firearms and musical instruments, for example, were sometimes designed and made with such care that they became works of art, simply because they were beautiful objects. Nowadays, however, the accelerating rate of development of technology and the increasing specialization of labour has led to a situation in which most of the things we use are designed and manufactured by somebody else. This means that designers have a profound effect on the quality of life, and a correspondingly profound obligation to do their job well. Good design means that an object will be used longer, with more efficiency and with more pleasure.

History of ergonomics Early in this century, many governments found it necessary to establish such offices as the Industrial Fatigue Research Board (later renamed the Industrial Health Research Board) in Britain. At about the same time, Americans such as F W Taylor and Henry FORD began to study industrial processes in order to make them more efficient; this became the science of TIME AND MOTION STUDY. Taylor and his followers did not pay much attention to the psychological aspect of industrial work, and their philosophy that factory workers should be rewarded with higher pay for more production, so that they can afford to buy the things that they make, frequently went out the window as employers wanted to increase efficiency (and lower costs) without raising wages. Gradually, however, industrial commissions and time study people have had to consult psychologists, architects and other professionals, and have come to recognize the importance of working conditions to the psychological well-being of the employee, because these affect his efficiency, his illness and absenteeism, and many other factors.

The development of the design philosophy now called ergonomics was slow during the period of world-wide economic depression during the 1930s, but received great impetus during World War 2. To illustrate the impact of the war, it may be useful to compare the early motor car with the modern aircraft.

Early cars were noisy, unreliable and subjected the driver and his passengers to a great deal of vibration and exposure to

Top right: in the early days of typewriting machines, the keyboard was designed so that the typist could not type faster than the action of the machine could respond. Nowadays, with typewriters having faster action, the keyboard has been redesigned, with the letters most often used being easiest to reach. Typing speeds averaging 35% higher will be possible, with less fatigue and fewer mistakes. The top picture shows the standard QWERTY keyboard; second from the top shows the DSK (Dvorak Simplified Keyboard).

Third from top: a set of cutlery designed for disabled people.

Bottom right: this bicycle was the first of the new small-wheeled bikes. It is stronger but lighter, has a lower centre of gravity, enabling heavy loads to be carried, has springing for comfort and is adjustable for riders of any height.

the elements. They were designed at the convenience of the the builder; sometimes the brake lever was actually located outside the driver's compartment, so that he had to reach out to set it. But early cars did not go very fast, and there were not very many of them; the owner of a car derived his pleasure partly from the ownership of a novelty.

By contrast, during World War 2 men were flying hundreds of miles an hour over long distances in circumstances of discomfort and extreme danger. Their seats had to be designed to provide as much comfort as possible in cramped circumstances; instruments had to be located so that they could be read at a glance; vital equipment such as oxygen masks in high-flying aircraft had to be well located and convenient to use. The human factor had to be taken into consideration, as well as cost, ease of manufacture, availability of raw materials, and other factors. In addition, ships and planes and other war material had to be produced in large numbers, using the most intense methods of mass production. During conditions of total war, the survival of a nation could depend on the design of its tools and the stress on its workmen and soldiers.

The word ergonomics was coined in 1949. It is derived from Greek roots, and literally means combining work with natural laws. Ergonomic design combines the insights and discoveries of physicians, biologists, psychologists, anthropologists, architects and other professionals, relating them to one another without placing undue value on any one discipline at the expense of the others. Ergonomic design is also called *biotechnology*, and is a part of engineering psychology; while engineering psychology can be misused, as when a product is designed with unnecessary features in order to persuade people to buy it, the point of ergonomic design is that the aesthetic value of a well-designed product or process arises out of consideration for the people who have to use it.

Since the war, the concept of ergonomic design has been extended to cover the whole of human physical existence, including consumer goods, domestic furniture, and much else. In order to consider the various aspects of ergonomic design, it will be useful to discuss these aspects separately.

The senses   There is evidence that a great deal of stress is caused by overloading of the senses. Hearing, vision, and the other senses are inputs into the nervous system, and if people are overloaded with sensory input they become irritable, frustrated and unable to concentrate.

Noise pollution is becoming more and more evident in today's world; many governments are passing laws to regulate the amount of noise which can be generated in a public place. Employers are required to provide protection in the form of

Top left: this tractor has some of the controls very badly placed, so that the driver has to reach way down to operate them. This causes fatigue and stress, and the vehicle is not under complete control if the driver has to operate these controls while it is moving. Early farm machines also had very hard seats.

Centre left: this combine harvester has a comfortable seat with back support in the right place, and all the controls conveniently placed for the driver. Once the driver is familiar with the controls he can use them without taking his eyes off the operating machinery.

Lower left: this fork lift truck has all the controls well placed and well designed, with diagrams on the tops of the knobs so that an inexperienced or illiterate driver can see what they are for. Visibility is also good from the driver's seat.

DIAGRAM VISUAL INFORMATION LTD

ear plugs for people who have to work in noisy areas. A loud noise can damage an eardrum, but most hearing loss is caused by progressive deterioration of the inner ear, caused by constant exposure to noise: the part of the hearing that is damaged will be the frequency range of the offending sound. Many men have lost part of their hearing as a result of prolonged exposure to gunfire during military training.

The physiology of hearing has been intensively studied, but less is known about the psychological stress induced by noise pollution. The designers of architectural space and consumer goods have to be able to deal with it. Furniture, carpets and curtains can all absorb sound, and rooms can be built with walls that absorb nearly all of it. The complete absence of sound, however, is not desirable either; the ears apparently need some small amount of background sound to distract them.

From the point of view of the designer, sound control is often out of his hands. Pneumatic drills for breaking concrete can be built which are relatively quiet, but this makes them more expensive, and contractors and local governments are reluctant to buy them for that reason. Much of sound control requires common sense and maintenance, for example the exhaust systems of automobiles. There is much that the designer can do, however, to prevent the generation of unnecessary noise. A machine designer will avoid mounting an electric motor or a gearbox on a large, hollow part of a machine, because this will amplify the sound; alternatively, the hollow part of the machine can be stuffed with sound deadening material, such as foam blocks. Rubber insulators between machine components are also used.

The designers of audio equipment must try to provide as wide a range of usable frequency response as possible, without peaks of excessive distortion. Otherwise the listener's ears will

Diagrams based on Henry Dreyfuss's ergonomic data for a seated woman at a typewriter, a man seated in a car and a woman in a kitchen. The original data has been simplified to give a clear idea of the kind of information designers and manufacturers use in the planning of cars and office and kitchen equipment.

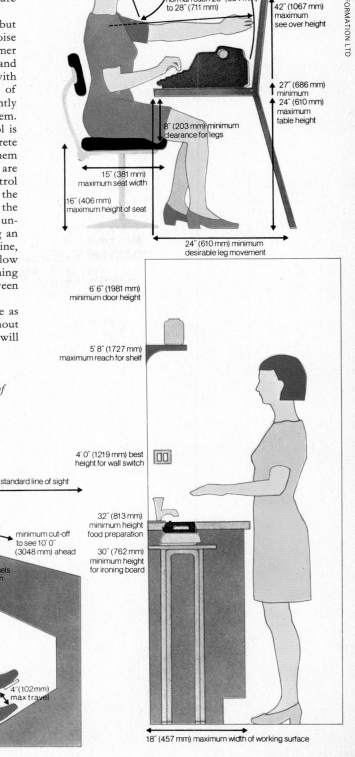

get tired of making the adjustments, and he will turn off his radio or record player, possibly without realizing that he is a victim of *listening fatigue*.

Vision is an aspect of design where a great deal can be done. Lights in a room, which at first appear to be adequate, will result in discomfort if they are a bit too bright or not bright enough. If there is too much glare it will be made worse by reflection on machinery or tabletops. If the lights flicker, even if the flicker is not quite noticeable, the result will be psychological stress and inability to concentrate on the part of the individual. In some instances people have suffered severe depression from living in rooms with bare light bulbs.

Measuring the light, however, is not all there is to ergonomic lighting; for efficiency at work and at home, many factors should be considered. The available light in a room depends upon the size and shape of the room and the colour of the walls as well as the location of windows and lights. Glare can be overcome to a certain extent by providing dull finishes on painted surfaces. There must be adequate contrast; for example a machine operator or a student reading a book should have more light on his work than on the immediate surroundings, or he will be distracted. On the other hand, a lampshade which blocks out too much light will provide too great a contrast. Other aspects which must be taken into consideration when designing lighting for work or play are persistence of vision, location of objects which must be visually referred to, and the incidence of defective colour vision in the population.

Human skin and muscles are sensitive organs which quickly become aware of poorly designed furniture, inconvenient location of appliances, poorly balanced tools, uncomfortable temperature and humidity, and many other considerations. When a machine operator says, 'This feels just right', he means that his machine and its controls are well designed. Controls such as levers and buttons should be located so that they can be operated by the machinist without taking his eyes off his work. A control lever in the cab of a crane, for example, should move forward or sideways according to the direction in which the boom will move. The response of the controls should be positive without being too quick. In the kitchen, ergonomic design means that sinks and work surfaces will be conveniently located, and some thought given to the actual sequence of steps in preparing a meal. Work surfaces must not be too high or too low, to prevent backaches.

There can be nothing worse for a student or an office worker than an uncomfortable chair. Anatomical studies can be used in the design of good furniture. The seat and the back of a chair must be firm enough to provide support, and designed to provide it in the right places. The chair must not be too high or too low, or the individual will be forced to adopt a poor posture in order to reach the floor with his feet; this is why office chairs and piano stools are often adjustable.

The senses of smell and taste are senses that most people can protect for themselves; nevertheless, designers today must resist the temptation to use chemicals to disguise unpleasant sensations or to provide imitation pleasant ones. A good example of the constructive use of the sense of smell is the addition of a peculiar smell to natural gas, which itself has no odour, so that leaks can easily be detected.

An example of the sort of pitfall a designer can fall into is the use of tinted glass in car windscreens. Car manufacturers will not paint their products dull colours, and sunlight reflected on the bonnet [hood] can be blinding. There is also the familiar problem of an approaching car with its bright lights on at night. But some of the various kinds of tinted or filtering glass which have been used to solve this problem have also cut down on night vision, a dangerous side effect. Solutions to design problems are not always as easy as they seem to be at first; the effects of the solutions must also be considered.

Architectural space

The subtle character of architectural space is one of the most important responsibilities of the architect. When he designs a building, he should be aware of all the subtle things that influence behaviour. When a person walks into a room, as for example the lobby of an office block, he is psychologically and emotionally affected by the size and shape of the room, the colour of the walls, the sound level in the room, the distance he has to travel to reach the receptionist's desk, and other factors. The company using the building can ask the architect to design it in such a way as to welcome visitors and make them feel as though they are invited inside. The type of fixtures in the room will determine whether or not visitors feel inclined to loiter there. If the room will be visited by a steady flow of traffic, as in a bank or a personnel department for example, the room and its fixtures can be designed to encourage the most convenient traffic flow. An expensive restaurant may want to encourage people to feel comfortable, while a lunch counter in a business district may want to discourage people from lingering over their coffee, so as to have the greatest possible turnover of trade during the peak hours of business.

Much of this is really engineering psychology. The ergonomic aspect is perhaps more immediately appreciable in the area of domestic architecture. If a flat [apartment] is designed so rooms are located adjacent to one long hallway, the people who use the rooms will spend a lot of time walking up and down that hallway, and people using various rooms will feel separated from one another, more so than if the flat were designed with all the rooms surrounding a central area. The environmental aspect of architecture has a profound effect on the sense of well-being, or lack of it. A direct correlation has been discovered, for example, between the number of flats opening onto a hallway in a public housing project and the rate of crime or vandalism in that project. If there are too many doors on a hallway, the lower income people who are housed in such buildings will feel depersonalized, as though they are living in a cell block rather than in housing designed for human beings, and they will behave accordingly, though they may not themselves perceive the reason for their feelings of frustration.

One well-known project in the United States was supposed to be the very latest thing in public housing. Much was made of the fact that it was constructed of materials that would need a minimum of maintenance. The residents of the buildings felt as though they had no control over their environment, and were surrounded by hard, unyielding surfaces, as though the character of the buildings was more important than the character of the people. The flats in the project were all designed so that mothers could not look out the window and keep an eye on their children at play, and so the open areas around the buildings were abandoned to vandals and muggers. There was no place in the architecture for residents to rub shoulders and chat with each other on a summer evening, as they had done in front of the tenement houses which the new project had replaced. Within a few months, the project had been reduced to a shambles by the frustrated residents, a profound example of what happens when the human factor is left out.

In the world of today, the quality of life is largely determined by designers. It is their great responsibility to design for people.

EROSION CONTROL

Erosion is the process of displacement of soil materials from the surface of the earth. It results principally from the passage of wind, water or ice over or against the land surface. Erosion by ice occurs in sparsely populated areas, and is of little economic or social consequence. Erosion by wind and water is widespread, and in fact is exacerbated by modification of the natural environment for economic exploitation.

A very large area of land surface may be subject to erosion by wind and rainfall, depending on factors such as climate and vegetation. Water erosion may be restricted to river channels or coastlines where the water and the land abut.

Control of soil erosion

Erosion by wind is confined to areas of relatively flat land where rainfall is sparse, or to flat areas which are heavily cultivated. In such areas, winds are strong and frequent, and there is not enough water in the soil to cause a cohesive effect. The speed of the wind can be reduced by *windbreaks*. A windbreak will reduce the speed of the wind at ground level for a distance of about five times its height on the windward side and twenty to thirty times on the leeward. The windbreak must, however, have a certain permeability to the wind, or serious turbulence (EDDY CURRENTS) may result around the ends of the windbreak, which will result in local erosion.

Windbreaks usually consist of rows of trees planted at right angles to the prevailing winds. For maximum effectiveness the rows should be no more than 500 m (about 540 yards) apart. Natural windbreaks have certain drawbacks; they compete with crops for moisture, nutrients and space, they may harbour pests, and at the time of the year when crops are not growing the foliage on the trees may not be dense enough to protect the soil from the wind. Sometimes scientifically designed artificial windbreaks of wood or substitute materials are used.

The surface of the ground is best protected from erosion by vegetation. This reduces wind speed at ground level and the roots help to bind together the particles of soil; the absence of vegetation is the reason cultivated soil is particularly subject to erosion during the soil preparation and sowing season. Recent methods of sowing crops allow sowing to be done directly into the stubble and waste plant matter left from the last growing season, a technique known as *stubble mulching*. *Strip farming*, a method of cultivating alternate strips 100 to 200 m (325 to 650 ft) wide, not only prevents wearing out the soil of nutrients by over farming it, but also helps prevent erosion, because the planted strips act as windbreaks. It is also possible to protect the soil by spraying it with bitumen emulsion; this is an especially useful technique in areas where a very sparse rainfall restricts the growth of a continuous vegetation cover.

The intensity of soil erosion by water depends on the velocity as well as the volume of water flow over the ground, and therefore is worst in areas of steep slopes and heavy rainfall. Here again, stubble mulching is useful, because it reduces rain-splash erosion, which results from the impact of rain drops on the ground, and also retards surface water flow. The use of *cover crops* is also widespread. In the tropics this may be a perennial tree beneath which other crops are grown; in more temperate climates a cover crop will be a winter annual which protects the bare ground when crops are not growing.

PHOTRI

Left: one technique for reducing soil erosion on hillsides and long slopes is to introduce terracing. Each level has a carefully positioned channel to catch the water and these lead to a central gully running down the hillside. The surface is made to slope slightly downwards so that the water at each level runs to the edge to the channel.

Right: here on the west coast of the island of Sylt at Schleswig-Holstein in Germany, coastal protection is achieved using these 'tetrapods'. These are reinforced concrete blocks cast into a three dimensional shape with four equally spaced 'spokes'. Tetrapods interlock and form a rough and broken 'front' on which the waves dissipate their energy.

Below: contour ploughing, where a hillside is ploughed along the contours of the hill, also helps to prevent soil erosion.

On slopes *contour ploughing* is practised. Ploughing along the contour rather than up and down the slope reduces the total run-off because water is stored in the furrow rather than channelled by it. (Channelling of run-off down a furrow results in a rapid erosion causing *gullies*.) Soil erosion can be reduced more than 50% by contour ploughing.

Terracing of hillsides is another contour technique. A system of ditches and embankments is constructed along the contour so as to direct run-off on a low gradient path to the edge of fields where it is drained off into prepared channels. Terracing is an ancient agricultural practice found in hilly areas of southern and eastern Asia, and is being adopted on a large scale by other countries.

River erosion Large scale erosive activity of rivers and streams is likely to be restricted to periods of peak flow following heavy rainfall or melting of ice and snow at higher altitudes. Control aims to reduce the intensity of run-off into the stream system, and is often the same thing as FLOOD CONTROL. Measures controlling soil erosion on the land near the river banks help to control peak flows; in addition, *afforestation* is frequently carried out. A woodland cover, especially near the headwater sections of a river, interrupts much of the run-off and lowers the level at the peak. Peak flows are also controlled by *dams*, which regulate the flow by filling up during peak periods; the water can be slowly discharged when the peak is past. Where erosion by running water is the major problem, the control uses a scheme of combined soil erosion control and river control.

Where erosion of stream banks is a problem, walls or embankments are constructed to replace the vulnerable natural bank. The erosion problem is usually concentrated on the outside bank of a bend in the river, and it is there where protection is most often needed.

Coastal erosion Coastal erosion can be spectacular, and the cost of controlling it very high. Fortunately only restricted areas of coastline need protection, usually areas of urban development in places where soft rock is exposed to erosive attack.

In many areas natural protection is afforded by beaches of sand or gravel; the slope of a beach dissipates the energy of waves. Beaches, however, are extremely unstable, and the material migrates alongshore. *Groynes* are constructed to impede this movement and to encourage the buildup of the beach. Groynes are barriers built out from the high tide mark, usually at right angles to the shore. They interfere with the longshore drift, each groyne collecting material on its updrift side. *Boxed groynes* are a more unusual attempt to build up material. These are a network of shallow, closely spaced

Below : sand dunes are particularly vulnerable to wind erosion and can be stabilized effectively by planting. Here a tough grass, suited to the conditions, provides a network of roots below and cover above.

ZEFA/PICTOR

groynes with elements both parallel and at right angles to the shoreline, forming a series of box sections. Beach material is thrown into the boxes by waves but the boxes inhibit movement of it during destructive storms. Linking groynes to sills out at sea encourages nature to build beaches; sand is deposited by waves breaking over the sills, but the water can flow back out.

On some coastal areas of North and South America, a new development of groynes in the form of self-sealing plastic bags has been successfully installed. The bags are designed to be of a given porosity according to local requirements; the waves deposit sand on the installation and the water filters through. Pyramid groynes built of these bags are often more successful than standard vertical groynes.

Sea walls or banks are an additional method of coastal defence. Walls which gently slope break the force of incoming waves and do not have to withstand the full force of storm waves. In resort areas, walls with nearly vertical faces are sometimes built because they take up less space; these are sometimes designed with a 'nose' at the top to throw the wave back instead of allowing it to splash over the wall. The beach in front of a sea wall will eventually be destroyed unless the wall is combined with groynes; the foundation of the wall itself will also be eroded.

The use of groynes or walls must be carefully engineered; erosion is often made worse at the ends of the protecting structures. Groynes especially, by preventing natural drift, may protect one section of beach but cause the next to be completely destroyed by depriving it of drifting materials.

For that matter, all erosion can be defined as a natural ongoing process of land sculpture and development that has been going on throughout all of geological time. Man may wish to reduce it or control it in a given area, but he cannot hope to stop it. What man must be particularly aware of is the need to control erosion that he induces by his own modification of the landscape.

ESCALATOR

The modern escalator provides the most efficient method of moving large numbers of people from one level to another at a controlled and even rate. In its simplest form it consists of a series of individual steps mounted between two endless chains which move upwards or downwards within a rigid steel truss frame.

The pioneers of the escalator were Jesse Reno and Charles Seeberger, whose designs were produced independently in the early 1890s, and in 1900 escalators were installed in Paris and New York. The first modern type of escalator, however, did not appear until 1921, incorporating the best features of both the Reno and Seeberger designs, and today escalators are commonplace in railway stations, airports, department stores and anywhere that a speedy and reliable service is required.

Most standard escalators are factory prefabricated and transported to the site in one piece, although they can be readily divided into three main sections: the top section, the centre section and tracks, and the bottom section.

Top section The top section houses the electrically powered driving machine and most of the controlling switchgear. The driving machine consists of an AC induction motor (see ELECTRIC MOTOR) running at around 1000 revs/min and driving the escalator through a worm type reduction GEAR. The main brake is spring-loaded into its 'on' position, being held 'off' by a DC electromagnet to enable the escalator to run. This arrangement is thus 'fail-safe', as in the event of a power supply failure the electromagnet will be de-energized and the brake will be applied by the springs. A hand winding wheel and a manual brake release lever allow the escalator to be moved by hand if necessary.

Below: an early Reno type of escalator, based on the design first patented by Jesse W Reno in 1891. As there were no actual steps on this type of escalator, the angle of incline had to be kept relatively small to make it easier to use.

The controlling unit includes rectifiers to provide the DC supply to the brake, a contactor to start the motor, and control relays linked to safety switches which will stop the machine in the event of an overload, drive chain breakage, or an obstruction to the steps or handrail. The controller is also linked to the key-operated starting switches and the emergency stop buttons, and contains a device to prevent an up-travelling escalator from reversing its direction of travel in the event of drive mechanism failure. To reduce wear and running costs some escalators are fitted with speed control devices that run the machine at half speed when no passengers are using it. Photoelectric sensors are fitted at each end to switch the escalator to full speed when a passenger steps on and to return it to half speed when all the passengers are cleared.

Centre and bottom sections The bottom section carries the step return idler sprockets (toothed wheels around which the chain turns), step chain safety switches and curved track sections to carry the motion of the escalator from the horizontal plane into the angle of climb, which is usually 30 to 35°. Between the top and bottom sections runs a welded box-type structure which carries the straight track sections.

The steps on which the passengers stand are assembled from aluminium pressure die castings and steel pressings mounted on a frame, usually of cast aluminium, which runs on rollers on the main track sections and is driven by the two main chains, one on each side. Foothold on the step surface is provided by a cleated board faced with aluminium or rubber.

The moving handrails are made from layers of canvas covered with a rubber or plastic moulding. They run in continuous loops in T-shaped guides along the tops of the balustrades, at a speed closely linked with that of the steps. The

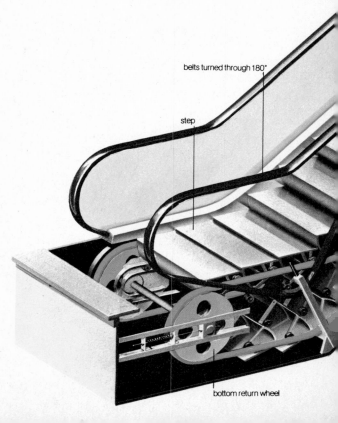

belts turned through 180°

step

bottom return wheel

balustrades and their skirtings are designed to allow a smooth passage for the steps, and all joints are securely masked. The running clearance of the steps has to comply with strict safety standards and the *combplates* (the metal teeth which project at the top and bottom of the fixed escalator base and provide the link between the moving treads and floor level) incorporate safety switches that will stop the escalator if any object becomes caught between the steps and the combplate.

Left: an escalator installation at Roselands shopping centre in New South Wales, Australia.

The tread width may be from two to four feet (0.6 to 1.2 m), and the speed of the operation from 90 to 180 ft/min (27 to 54 m/min). Running at 145 ft/min (44 m/min) a single escalator can carry up to 10,000 passengers an hour, and will be powered by a 100 hp motor. A variation of the escalator, the TRAVELA-TOR, is a horizontal continuous rubber belt used for moving passengers around such places as airport terminals and railway stations.

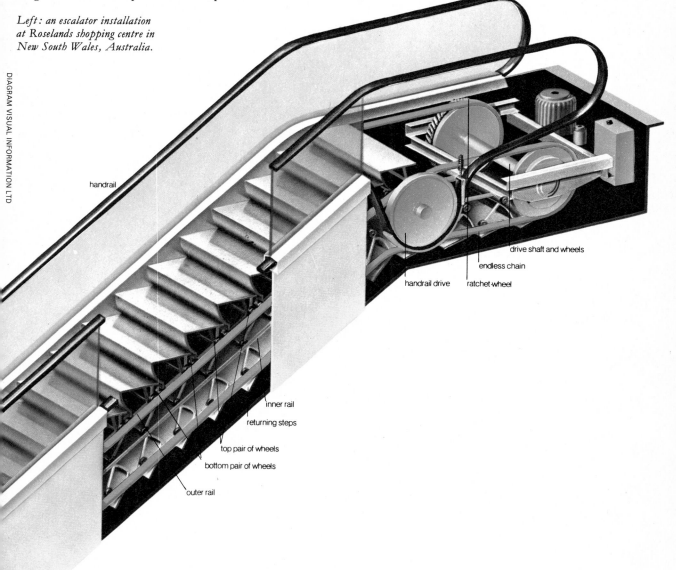

handrail

drive shaft and wheels

endless chain

handrail drive   ratchet wheel

inner rail

returning steps

top pair of wheels

bottom pair of wheels

outer rail

DIAGRAM VISUAL INFORMATION LTD

Above: a section through an escalator, which consists of a continuously moving series of individual steps on an endless chain. Each step moves on small wheels along rails. These are positioned so that the steps fold to give a horizontal surface at the top and bottom. The handrail is a moving belt of rubber and canvas.

ETHER

The concept of the ether—not to be confused with the anaesthetic of the same name—is one of the oldest in physics. The early natural philosophers postulated the existence of an invisible, intangible substance that pervades all space, empty and occupied alike. The word 'ether' is derived from the Greek *aether* meaning 'cosmic' or 'essential' air and was regarded by many Greek philosophers as the fifth 'element', the others being earth, water, air and fire.

The existence of such a medium was thought to be as much a philosophical as physical necessity. It was argued that a completely empty space, containing absolutely nothing, could not be perceived, and hence could not be said to exist. Since we do experience the idea of space, even in a vacuum, there must be something which fills the whole of space. Because it permeates even solid bodies, this medium, the ether, was thought to be very tenuous.

The great physicists Descartes and NEWTON developed the idea of the ether to account for the phenomenon of 'action at a distance'. Descartes realized that heat and light from the Sun must travel through the vacuum of 'space' before reaching the Earth, and he thought there must be a medium to transmit it, just as sound is transmitted by the air. Newton's Law of GRAVITATION required that two bodies will attract each other by gravity, even at a distance and in a vacuum, and it seemed there must be a 'go-between' which transmitted this force. The ether's properties were thus extended to conveying heat, light and gravitational forces.

In the early nineteenth century, the discovery of the optical phenomena of interference and DIFFRACTION led to the wave theory of light, and the discovery of POLARIZATION of light meant that these waves must be *transverse* (that is, the ether would move from side to side as light waves passed by, rather than backwards and forwards). The implication is that if transverse waves, with wavelengths of thousandths of a millimetre, travel at the speed of light in the ether, it cannot be tenuous, but must be a rigid solid with a density of 1000 tons per cubic millimetre!

MAXWELL's electromagnetic theory explained light, and all ELECTROMAGNETIC RADIATION, as being due to simultaneous electrical and magnetic waves, and from his equations he could deduce the speed of light, which seemed to be a fundamental constant. It was natural to assume that light moved at this speed relative to the fixed ether, and that as the Earth moved in

Below: the famous Michelson-Morley experiment of 1887 designed to detect the presence of an ether 'wind' passing over the surface of moving earth. A beam of light is directed onto a half-silvered mirror. Half the beam passes straight through and half is reflected at right angles. Both are then reflected back to the mirror and on to a telescope where a series of light and dark interference fringes are seen. If the whole apparatus is then rotated through 90° then the direction of the ether wind with respect to the light paths would be changed and the difference in time taken for the light beams to traverse the paths in the new direction registered by a shift in the interference fringes. In fact the experiment was carried out with increasingly sophisticated refinements and no shift could be detected. Scientists were forced to accept that the ether did not exist.

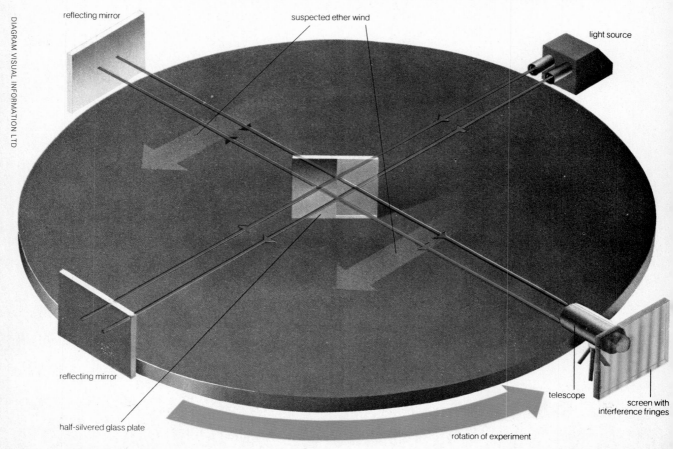

reflecting mirror

suspected ether wind

light source

reflecting mirror

half-silvered glass plate

telescope

screen with interference fringes

rotation of experiment

its orbit about the Sun, the speed of light would change according to the direction in which it was measured. In 1887, two American physicists, Michelson and Morley, tried to measure the motion of the Earth relative to the ether by sending a beam of light along two paths of equal length at right angles to each other. At the end of each path a mirror reflected the light back to the observer, who could measure any difference in the time taken to travel the two paths. If the Earth is moving through the ether, the beam of light travelling perpendicular to the direction of the Earth's motion would return more quickly than that travelling parallel to the Earth; but Michelson and Morley could find absolutely no difference. This seemed to imply that the Earth is stationary in the ether, and it was suggested that the Earth drags some of the ether with it as it moves round its orbit. This explanation was not very satisfactory and it was not until 1905 that the experimental result was explained. In this year EINSTEIN published his Special Theory of RELATIVITY, which stated that any observer, moving at any speed, would measure light as travelling at the speed predicted by Maxwell's equations. This implies that light is not transmitted by a fixed ether, and indeed, that any experiment to detect the ether would fail, just as the Michelson-Morley experiment did. In the same year Einstein also extended the QUANTUM THEORY, originally due to Max PLANCK, to the idea that light travels in quanta, or discrete packets of energy, which behave like particles as well as like waves. If light is composed of particles, then the idea of an ether in which the wave vibrates is unnecessary. Thus Einstein showed that the ether was both unobservable and unnecessary.

EXCAVATOR, hydraulic

Hydraulic excavators are among the most useful machines available to the construction industry. In capacity they range from small machines suitable for ditch cleaning to the largest which can lift and dump 20 tons of rock at a time, but the typical general purpose machines have a capacity of 1.5 or 2 tons. Many are mounted on pneumatic tyres [tires], but most run on crawler type tracks. The smaller designs are often based on derivatives of agricultural TRACTORS, but the majority are purpose-built from the ground up.

Engine and hydraulics The usual power source of a hydraulic excavator is a modified automotive DIESEL ENGINE, but with high pressure oil pumps fitted in place of the usual clutch-torque converter-gearbox transmission assembly. The boom movements are made by double-acting piston and cylinder rams, and HYDRAULIC motors power the slewing motion and drive the crawler tracks. Wheeled machines usually have a geared drive for travelling.

The hydraulic systems are controlled by valves fitted into the oil lines that connect the pumps with the rams, and the driver operates the valves by means of levers and pedals in the cab. The larger machines usually have SERVOMECHANISMS to reduce the effort required from the driver. Oil pressures vary from one design to another, but typically range from 105 to 340 bar (1500 to 4850 psi).

Below: a wheeled excavator with a backhoe assembly at the rear and a loading shovel at the front. The driver has a separate seat and set of controls for operating the backhoe and the shovel.

FOTOLINK

Types of excavator

The common factor shared by all hydraulic excavators is a sturdily built boom with three or more hinged joints, which carries the digging implement. In all crawler and wheeled machines, other than the tractor-based designs, this boom is mounted on a *slewing platform* which also carries the operator's cabin and the engine and its ancillary components. The slewing platform is mounted on an undercarriage which comprises the running gear, and in all modern designs it is able to revolve continuously in either direction.

Tractor-based excavators have the digging attachment mounted at the rear, and a common adaptation permits the base of the boom to be moved bodily sideways. Thus although the boom swing is limited to only about half a circle, the machines can still work effectively in confined spaces. This type of excavator usually has a hydraulically operated loading shovel attached to its front end.

The hydraulic excavator began as, essentially, a trenching tool. In this form it is generally known as a *backhoe*, and it digs by pressing the leading edge of its bucket into the soil, then rotating and thus filling the bucket by means of the boom rams. The load is then raised by the boom, which is swung away from the excavation by the slewing motion. The load is dumped by contra-rotating the bucket.

Among the numerous attachments available to increase the versatility of the machines are special purpose buckets for light or dense materials, ditch cleaning and weed cutting; ripper teeth for breaking layered rock and paving; 'clamshell' buckets for sinking circular or square shafts; extension pieces to lengthen booms; and magnets and grabs for scrap metal handling.

The most important adaptation of the base machine, however, is the *face shovel*, in which the digging action is reversed so that the bucket is loaded by pushing forward rather than by being dragged back. This may be achieved by rearranging the standard boom components, but most machines use face shovel boom assemblies which are interchangeable as a whole with the backhoe assembly. Face shovels are usually used for hard, heavy digging, as for example in strip mining and quarry work.

The backhoe is invariably arranged to provide the maximum reach, digging depth and dumping height commensurate with machine stability and a reasonable working life. Wheeled machines often have hydraulically operated stabilizing arms to support the machine on sloping or uneven ground. Face shovels, however, stand close to their work and are rarely able to dig below ground level. Typically, they shovel material from the foot of a quarry face, slew through a quarter or half circle, and empty the material into a truck.

Since the immediate post-war years, when hydraulics technology was first seriously applied to EARTHMOVING MACHINES, the hydraulic excavator has steadily superseded the cable (wire rope) operated machines (such as the dragline excavator) for most small or medium sized tasks, but as yet it cannot compete with the larger rope operated equipment.

EXCHANGE REACTION (see chemistry)

EXCLUSION PRINCIPLE (see periodic table)

Below left: a wheeled tractor-type excavator. The stabilizing arms, which are hydraulically operated, are used to hold the machine steady during the digging operations, and are also extremely useful when the excavator is working on sloping or uneven surfaces as they can be adjusted independently to keep the machine level.

Below right: a crawler mounted slewing platform excavator, seen here with the platform swung through about 90°.

EXHAUST SYSTEM, car

The INTERNAL COMBUSTION ENGINE of a car gets its power from mixtures of petrol [gasoline] and air which are successively exploded inside it. The hot gases created by this series of explosions expand against the pistons to do the work and are then allowed to escape through an arrangement of pipes, the exhaust system. As the gases are not only poisonous but at a temperature of about 1700 °C (more than 3000 °F) and a pressure of about 100 psi (7 bar) when the exhaust valve opens, one of the main functions of such a system is to dispose of them without harm to the occupants of the car or to passers-by. Since the action of the engine results in a series of loud bangs, another function is to reduce the noise generated to an acceptable level.

An exhaust system starts with an assembly of several pipes collectively called a *manifold* (meaning 'many branched') bolted to the engine and usually converging to a single steel pipe which passes underneath the car to the silencer [muffler], the main noise-reducing component. The silencer is in turn connected to a short length of tailpipe which finishes at the rear of the car several inches above the ground. Sometimes an additional expansion chamber located near the manifold is fitted to absorb more exhaust noise.

Gaskets are fitted where the manifold is bolted to the engine and where the manifold pipe is bolted to the manifold, to ensure a tight connection and prevent the escape of gas and noise. The rest of the system is fastened together and suspended from the underside of the car by a variety of clamps. The entire system, especially the silencer, is exposed to the road surface and subject to a great deal of corrosion and vibration. It is often the first component of a car to fail. In an attempt to make their exhaust system last longer, one American car manufacturer tried coating the components with a ceramic material, but the coating was very brittle and prone to chipping. Longer lasting systems are made of aluminized or aluminium coated steel, or stainless steel, which is very expensive but lasts longest of all and may be cheapest in the long run.

The high temperature of the exhaust gases is reduced to a safe level by cooling in the several feet (2 to 3 m) of pipe which make up a typical system. (In cars with aircooled engines the exhaust system can provide warmth for interior heating.) The poisonous nature of the exhaust gases, mostly from carbon monoxide, is not a problem to the occupants of the car (except in a small, closed garage when it is very dangerous) so long as the exhaust system is completely gas-tight and does not leak fumes into the interior of the car. There is a low-pressure area immediately behind a moving car, however, which can cause fumes to be sucked back into it, so the exact location of the tailpipe and the proper sealing of the boot [trunk] lid or tailgate are also of importance. Exhaust gas toxicity is seldom an immediate danger to pedestrians in the open air, though in most countries, cars now have to conform to exhaust emission regulations, to ensure that dangerous pollutants are kept to a safe minimum.

For mass-produced engines, the exhaust manifold is usually a single unit made of cast iron, incorporating separate pipes from each cylinder or pair of cylinders which join together into a single outlet of larger diameter. The lengths and geometry of these manifold pipes determine the back-pressure on the engine and so affect its performance and economy. Hence the exhaust manifolds of more highly tuned or expensive engines are sometimes made of very gently curved separate steel pipes of carefully chosen length. When there are two banks of cylinders, as in a V8 engine, two exhaust manifolds are required, and these either lead to a pair or more of entirely separate exhaust systems or are joined to outlet pipes which

Below: the exhaust system of a motor car engine. Waste gases formed during the combustion cycle pass out through the manifold pipes and the silencer to the tail pipe and out to the rear of the car. The silencer [muffler] absorbs the sound waves produced by the individual cylinders as they discharge in turn into the system.

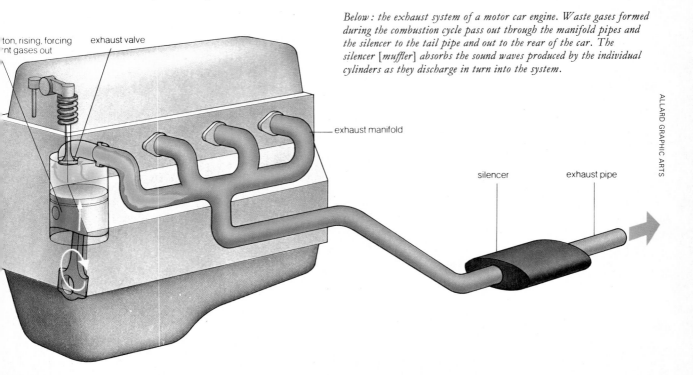

ton, rising, forcing
nt gases out

exhaust valve

exhaust manifold

silencer

exhaust pipe

ALLARD GRAPHIC ARTS

meet fairly close to the engine at a single final pipe.

The supersonic shockwaves of which exhaust noise is partly composed are reduced in intensity by allowing the gases to expand several times in succession, first in the separate expansion chamber if fitted, and then at perforations in tubes inside cavities within the silencer. The low frequency sound waves also generated are weakened by out-of-phase vibrations of the gases in the expansion chambers, which tend to cancel out the sound waves. In some silencers the perforated tubes are surrounded by an absorptive material such as glass wool which has a high resistance to air movement and cuts down the remaining high-frequency noise.

Cars built since 1970—and especially those sold in the USA—may have exhaust systems which have been modified to meet the pollution laws. In one such emission control system, air from an engine-driven pump is injected into the exhaust manifold to help the completion of the combustion process begun in the cylinder head so that the gases can become more completely consumed. In another system, a proportion of the exhaust gas may be fed back into the engine to dilute the incoming mixture, reduce combustion temperatures and minimize another pollutant. Other cars may use what are called *catalytic converters*, which purify the exhaust gases and are fitted instead of the silencer or in addition to it.

Below: two types of silencers made of stainless steel. The exhaust gases expand through the perforations and the frequency of the sound waves is broken into small patterns which tend to cancel each other out. The glass fibre packing helps sound absorption.

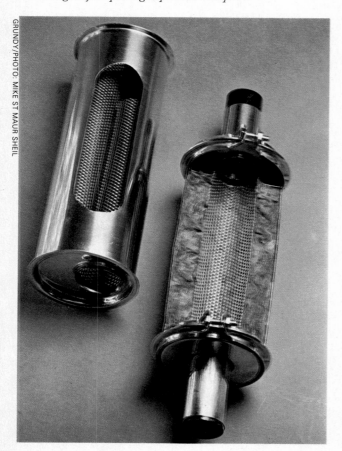

GRUNDY/PHOTO: MIKE ST MAUR SHEIL

EXPLOSIVES

The first pyrotechnic material to be used in war was GREEK FIRE, invented by Kallenikos in AD 673. Although not strictly an explosive, it was used with devastating success in several battles in the Mediterranean, and was a primitive but highly effective incendiary material probably based on petroleum oils and sulphur. Its secret was lost with the fall of the Byzantine Empire in AD 1453.

The origins of gunpowder (or black powder) are obscure, but the Chinese were probably aware of the properties of saltpetre (potassium nitrate) as early as the Chin Dynasty (221 to 207 BC), although they did not develop its use beyond the FIREWORK stage until about the 12th century. In the west this material was known as 'Chinese snow', and the first recorded Western experimenter to establish the formula for gunpowder was an English monk, Roger BACON. In AD 1245 he recorded it as a Latin anagram in his *De Secretis Operibus Artis et Naturae* (Secret Works of Art and Nature).

Its first use as a gun propellant followed in about 1320, and English troops used CANNON against the French at Crecy in 1346. The formula has changed somewhat since then, and today the proportions used are 75% saltpetre (potassium nitrate), 15% charcoal (carbon) and 10% sulphur. It is not now used as a gun propellant as it burns too quickly, about 400 metres (1312 ft) per second, its residue fouls the bore of the gun, and it produces too much smoke. On the other hand its combustion is too slow to produce the shattering effect of a high explosive. It is, however, widely used in fireworks and in blank cartridges, and it was used by the Russians in the retro-rockets of the planetary surface probe sent to Mars.

Explosion and detonation When an explosive substance is set off it undergoes rapid decomposition and releases large quantities of gas and heat. *Explosion* is a fast combustion, the burning spreading layer by layer through the material at the comparatively slow velocity of up to 400 metres (1312 ft) per second, and although its rate increases with increasing pressure, it can be controlled. This reaction is often called *deflagration*.

In a *detonation* reaction there is an extremely rapid burning which produces a supersonic shock, or detonating wave, in the explosive substance. The detonation velocity is a characteristic of the explosive material itself and is unchanged by changes in pressure. It is usually between 2000 and 9000 metres (6500 and 29,500 feet) per second. The detonation wave produces a very high pressure, about 650 tons per square inch (100,000 bar), and this exerts a severe shattering effect on anything in its path. The gases formed travel in the same direction as the detonation wave, so a low pressure region is created behind it. Once detonation has been started it cannot be stopped (see also DETONATOR).

Explosives which react by deflagrating are called 'low explosives' or 'propellants'; they generate gases at a slow enough rate for them to be used to propel ROCKETS or shells. Those which react by detonation have the ability to shatter and are called 'high explosives'. They are used in BOMBS and explosive shells, and in blasting operations like quarrying and mining.

Classification Explosives can be classified according to their properties and uses. In Britain, for example, there are seven classes: class 1, gunpowder; class 2, nitrate mixtures; class 3, nitro-compounds; class 4, chlorate mixtures; class 5, fulminates; class 6, AMMUNITION; and class 7, fireworks. There are other important forms of classification to define transport, storage and firefighting hazards.

The essential properties of explosives are the velocity of burning or detonation, the explosion temperature, the sensitivity, and the power. For the first three classes above, an absolute measurement is possible, but for the others it is usual to compare the explosive with a standard such as *picric acid*. Picric acid is taken to have a 'value' of 100, with more sensitive or less powerful explosives having values lower than 100. The more sensitive explosives with values of around 20 are used as detonators to initiate explosives. Their impulses can set off the intermediary charges (those of moderate sensitivity, about 60) which in turn will initiate the reactions in the main charges, which are the least sensitive.

Modern explosives The use of gunpowder as an explosive declined in the 19th century, and it was replaced by three main types of composition: those based on unstable molecules, such as the fulminates and azides; ammonium nitrate and the organic esters nitrocellulose, nitroglycerine and PETN; and the nitro-compounds, a large group which includes picric acid, TNT, tetryl and RDX.

In 1845 Schönbein nitrated cotton with a mixture of nitric and sulphuric acids to give nitrocellulose $(C_6H_7O_2(NO_3)_3)_n$. Until 1875, when Sir Frederick Abel devised a method of pulping the cotton to give a more stable product, there were many accidental explosions associated with its manufacture.

Below : one of the most common uses of explosives is in quarrying. Here a line of charges has been detonated to bring down a section of the face of a limestone quarry. The broken rock can be easily excavated and removed by power shovels and trucks.

Its properties depend on the degree of nitration, which is hindered by the fibrous nature of the cotton, and it is usually a mixture of the di- and tri-nitrates. It is easily gelled by solvents and can be then pressed into the required shape, for example cord, flake or tube. It is very sensitive when dry (with a rating of about 23), but less so when wet (about 120) yet can still be detonated. The velocities of detonation are 7300 (dry) and 5500 (wet) metres/second (23,950 and 18,000 feet/second respectively).

The highly dangerous explosive liquid *nitroglycerine* (sensitivity 13) was first prepared in 1846 by Sobrero in Turin by nitrating glycerol with a mixture of nitric and sulphuric acids. In 1865 Alfred NOBEL found that the liquid could be used safely if it was first absorbed into kieselguhr, a form of *diatomaceous earth* (formed by the fossil remains of a type of single-celled *algae*). He also succeeded in solidifying it by adding 8% nitrocellulose to form a gel. He named these famous explosives dynamite and blasting gelatine. Nitroglycerine $(C_3H_5N_3O_9)$ detonates at 7750 metres (25,426 feet) per second, has a power rating of 160, and an explosion temperature of 4427 °C (8000 °F).

PETN (*pentaerythritol tetranitrate*, $C_5H_8N_4O_{12}$) is a sensitive explosive (40) with a high power rating (166) and a detonation velocity of 8100 m (26,500 ft) per second. It can be used as an intermediary charge but it is extensively used in detonating cords where its small critical diameter enables it to maintain a detonating impulse over a great distance, despite low filling densities.

Picric acid was first prepared by Woulfe in 1771, a hundred years before Sprengel demonstrated that it could be detonated by a mercury fulminate cap. Prepared by the nitration of phenol, it was the first of a large series of aromatic nitro-compounds to be discovered. As it is much less sensitive than nitrocellulose or nitroglycerine, but just as powerful, it safely withstands the shock of discharge from a gun, and in 1888 it replaced gunpowder as a shell filling. Apart from its value as a standard, picric acid, $C_6H_2(NO_2)_3OH$, is little used today.

TNT, *trinitrotoluene*, $C_7H_5(NO_2)_3$, is made by reacting toluene with a nitrating mixture of nitric and sulphuric acids. Its sensitivity is 110, power rating 95, and its velocity of detonation 7000 m/sec (22,965 ft/sec). It is cheap and easy to make and widely used to fill shells and bombs, often being mixed with ammonium nitrate for such applications.

Tetryl, $C_7H_5N_5O_8$, is formed when dimethylaniline is nitrated. It requires careful extraction and preparation for use as an explosive, as it is powdery and toxic. It has a detonation velocity of 7300 m/sec (23,950 ft/sec), a power value of 120, and a sensitivity of 70, which makes it a good intermediary charge to transfer a detonating shock wave from a detonator to a main charge.

RDX, $(CH_2N.NO_2)_3$, also called *Hexögen* or *Cyclonite*, was discovered by the German Henning in 1899. It is the product of the nitration of *hexamethylenetetramine*, and is a very powerful explosive (167) with a high velocity of detonation, 8400 m/sec (27,560 ft/sec), and a moderate sensitivity of 55. It has many uses in the military and civil fields.

Applications

Inevitably explosives find their principal applications in war, and modern propellants stem from developments made in the 1880s. In 1884 the French engineer Vieille gelled nitrocellulose with an ether-alcohol solvent, then cut the sheets into flakes, and named it 'Poudre B' after General Boulanger. Nobel made *Ballistite* in 1888 by gelling nitrocellulose with nitroglycerine, and the English *Cordite* of 1889 was produced by Nobel's methods. As gun propellants

Below : the manufacture of dynamite. Originally pioneered by Nobel, this explosive basically consisted of 75% nitroglycerine and 25% kieselguhr. The composition of modern explosives is varied in order to adjust the blasting power for the different purposes for which it is required. Common salt can be added to reduce the shattering power to make it safe for use in mines.

ALLARD GRAPHIC ARTS

glycerine

sulphuric acid
sulphur trioxide

nitric acid

cooling water in

cooling water out

mixture stirred

nitration

waste gas

consumed nitric acid

soda solution

neutralisation
& purification

mixture stirred

salts   nitrocellulose

washing liquor

finished explosive

these substances burn quite slowly, yet if the constituents are suitably ignited they detonate at many thousands of metres per second.

Shaping the explosive into a hollow cone and lining it with metal produces a 'hollow charge', which focuses the explosive effect into a jet powerful enough to penetrate substantial thicknesses of steel (see ARMOUR PIERCING SHELL). The impulse produced on detonating an explosive can easily be used to bond metals together, or to press them into the shape of a former laid below. This technique is used to make such things as dental plates and radomes (the protective domes often fitted over radar antennas).

Explosives are widely used in mining; in the UK the annual use is about 50,000 tons for COAL MINING, each pound (0.45 kg) of explosive winning about four tons of coal. Canal excavation, harbour deepening, and DEMOLITION are other fields in which large quantities of explosives are used. In seismic prospecting, for oil for example, shock waves generated by the detonation of a charge travel into the strata below and are reflected or refracted by the geological features in the area. By detecting these reflected waves a picture of the underlying geological formation of the site can be built up.

An unusual application is that of quenching oil and gas well fires. The largest ever, at Gassi Touil in the Sahara, which had burned for five months, was put out by 'Red' Adair of Texas using 550 lb (249 kg) of dynamite, for a fee of $1,000,000.

Below: a series of four photographs showing the development of the detonation wave in a block of solid explosive, in this case a mixture of RDX and TNT. The sequence runs from left to right, and shows frames 2, 3, 4 and 7 of a high speed sequence that was photographed with a time interval of two microseconds (millionths of a second) between each of the frames.

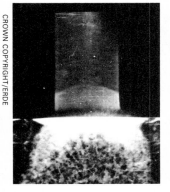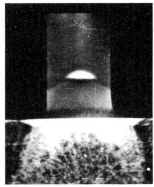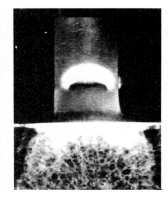

CROWN COPYRIGHT/ERDE

ICI

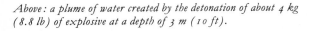

Above: a plume of water created by the detonation of about 4 kg (8.8 lb) of explosive at a depth of 3 m (10 ft).

Right: a composite metal plate, made of a sheet of carbon steel laminated with a cladding sheet of aluminium bronze. The sheets are placed a little way apart, and explosive is spread across the cladding and detonated to force the two together, producing a permanent bond.

EXPOSURE METER

When taking a photograph, the photographer has to make sure that the correct amount of light passes through the lens aperture and shutter of the CAMERA on to the light-sensitive film. If there is too little, the picture will be too dark, or *underexposed*; if there is too much, it will be too light or *overexposed*.

To accurately record his subject on to film, the photographer therefore uses an exposure meter, an instrument which measures the intensity of the light and either indicates or automatically produces the correct exposure for the picture to be taken.

In the early days of photography, this 'correct exposure' was found by trial and error, or by the photographer's own experience. Printed charts and tables were available which gave a rough guide to exposure in average lighting conditions (like the tables packed with modern films today).

A more accurate measuring system came with the invention of the *actinometer*. A light sensitive paper was placed in the meter and put in front of the subject. By comparing the tone of discoloration caused by the light falling on the paper with a separate, pre-printed tint card, timing the process, and referring to tables, an exposure was found for the subject itself.

This rather time consuming method was superseded by the *extinction meter*, basically a tube with a dark interior and an aperture at each end. A transparent strip graded in blackness, and overprinted with black numerals, was placed between the ends of the meter. The subject was viewed through the tube and a numeral found that, in relation to the illumination level, merged with its background tone. This number was transferred

by calculation to give an approximate camera setting.

The photoelectric exposure meter was introduced in America in 1932, and is a far more advanced and accurate instrument. It measures the light level falling on a light sensitive surface (a PHOTOELECTRIC CELL) in electrical terms. In separate (off camera) meters, the photocell activates a needle over a scale of *exposure values*, which can be read out as a range of shutter and aperture settings. The photographer then adjusts the camera accordingly. When the meter is built into the camera itself, the needle can be designed to appear within the viewfinder. In this case in semi-automatic cameras, the cell is linked electrically or mechanically to either the aperture or shutter, leaving the operator one adjustment to complete the setting. On fully automated cameras, it is linked to both.

Types of cell In the *selenium* cell, the light falls on a photocell which has two electrically conductive layers, sandwiching a layer of selenium. The light creates an electrical potential between the two layers in proportion to its intensity, and this current is registered on a sensitive AMMETER by a needle. The *cadmium sulphide* (CdS) cell is more sensitive to light than the selenium type, and can be used in duller lighting conditions. This cell is not electrically self generating, however; the electrical RESISTANCE of the cell varies with the intensity of the light, and a battery (usually a long-life mercury cell) is needed to power the circuit.

Using a meter An exposure meter is not infallible, and unless used correctly, will give inaccurate results. The most common method of using the meter is to gauge a general or overall level of brightness. This will take into account the darker

JOHN BISHOP

Labels: shutter/ASA dial, ammeter, printed circuits, resistors, CDS cells, pentaprism, aperture linkage, meter switch, mirror, batteries

Left: the built in exposure meter system of the Nikon F2 uses two CdS cells arranged to weight the reading to the centre of the lens' field of view. The meter reading, visible in the viewfinder, varies with the brightness of the scene and must be centred by adjusting shutter speed and aperture. This would mean darkening the field of view, making the shot hard to set up and focus. Instead, the meter is fed a reading which is adjusted electrically to take lens, shutter and film speed settings into account. The aperture ring is linked by gears to a ring of carbon resistance material. The combined shutter and film (ASA) speed is linked to another ring carrying a 'brush' which also tracks along the resistance ring. The current in the cell circuit is passed through the resistance between this brush and a fixed one on top of the assembly. The amount of carbon track between the two brushes thus depends on all three variable settings. Resistors and printed circuits are used to trim the battery output to give constant results and to balance the CdS cells.

Right: the Weston Master V has a selenium cell, used for its constant accuracy. The acceptance angle can be varied from 80° to 55° by moving the hinged outer baffle plate. Buttons lock the scale movements and the meter needle.

and lighter parts of the subject, and give an average reference for exposure. Having been set for the *speed* (sensitivity) of the type of film in use, the meter is pointed towards the subject and an average reflected light value is read off.

Another method is to use an *invercone*, a translucent attachment which is placed over the photocell. This reduces the reading somewhat but instead of measuring the reflected light, the *incident* light falling on the subject is used. This method overcomes problems caused by one part of the picture being much brighter or darker than the subject, thus giving a false reflected light reading.

The exposure value (EV) is a combination of shutter speed and aperture, and its choice depends on the depth of field and movement of a particular subject. For example the camera may be marked in apertures (*f* numbers) between *f*3.5 and *f*22, and have shutter speeds of between one second and one thousandth of a second. The meter will indicate a number of these combinations, all theoretically correct (*f*8 at 1/500 second being equivalent to *f*11 at 1/250, since although the speed has been halved, the aperture has been made smaller accordingly).

Meters read a particular area of the subject in front of them. This is the *acceptance angle*, and will differ between models. More advanced meters may read a general area, and also have the facility to take a spot reading of a small part of the subject.

Right: an exposure meter being used in the studio to measure the reflected light from the subject. To check the incident light, the meter, fitted with an invercone, is held near the subject but facing the other way, towards the light source.

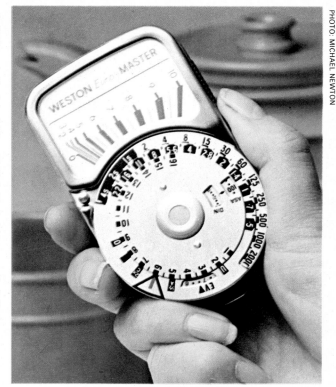

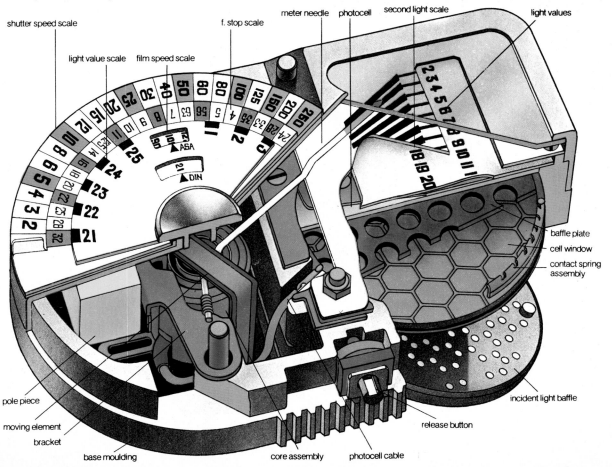

shutter speed scale

light value scale   film speed scale

f. stop scale

meter needle   photocell   second light scale   light values

baffle plate

cell window

contact spring assembly

pole piece

moving element

bracket

base moulding

core assembly   photocell cable

release button

incident light baffle

EXTRUSION

Extrusion is a useful process for shaping both metal and plastic products, notably rods, tubes and various simple solid and hollow shapes, by forcing them through a die, in much the same way as icing [frosting] is forced from the nozzle of cake decorating equipment.

Plastic extrusion Plastics are extruded by being forced through orifices or 'dies' which give them a particular shape. Flat sheet, pipe, tubular film (plastic bags), coated wires, and profiles such as domestic curtain rails are some of the many products manufactured by this means. The PLASTICS used are predominantly of the thermoplastic type, which includes polyethylene, polypropylene, polystyrene, nylon, polyvinyl chloride and many more. Such materials are extruded in the highly-viscous molten state, typical processing temperatures being in the range 150 to 300 °C (302 to 572 °F).

Extrusion machines must be capable of both melting the plastics and generating extrusion pressures of the order of several hundred atmospheres at the dies. They also have to perform other functions such as the mixing in of colouring matter and other additives, occasionally reinforcing agents such as glass fibres. Another important requirement is for continuous steady operation.

The most commonly used machines are single screw extruders. The plastic material, normally in granular or powder form, is fed via a hopper to a coarse-pitched ARCHIMEDEAN SCREW rotating inside an electrically heated barrel.

The screw generally has three distinct sections. In the feed section, which conveys solid material from under the hopper, the screw channel depth is constant and relatively large. The subsequent compression section has a uniformly reducing channel depth and is intended to compact the plastic and force it into contact with the barrel to encourage melting. Melting is achieved mainly by a combination of heat conducted from the barrel and heat generated by intense shearing in the molten layer formed between the barrel and the solid material. As its name suggests, the third or metering section of the screw, in which the channel depth is constant and relatively small, is intended to control the output from the extruder in terms of quantity, steadiness and homogeneity. The relative motion between the screw and barrel creates an efficient mixing action in the now molten plastic, and is capable of generating the pressures required for extrusion.

Extruders range in screw diameter from about one to twelve

Below left: a typical plastics extruder designed to handle rigid cellular PVC. Powdered PVC is fed into the machine, melted, forced through a die and cooled, emerging as skirting board sections, which have the density, texture and working properties of wood.

Bottom left: apart from wire and rods, a wide selection of metal blanks can be readily formed by extrusion processes.

Bottom right: helical extrusion is used for reducing billets directly to wire. In a single operation it combines hydrostatic extrusion, normal extrusion and an intermediate stage similar to lathe turning. The massive hydrostatic extrusion cylinder can be seen at the top. A copper billet stands on the left ready for loading.

inches, and give outputs from a few pounds to several tons per hour. Barrels and screws are made from hardened steel to minimize wear, since for efficient operation the clearances between them must be small. Screws are normally run at about 100 rev/min, driven by electric motors via reduction gears. Any air entering with the solid feedstock is forced out by the subsequent compaction. Some plastics tend to contain volatile contaminants such as unconverted monomer from the polymerization process, so modified screw designs are used which allow the use of a vent about half way along the barrel. There is normally a filter for solid debris between the screw and die.

The screw extruder also forms the basis of several other plastics processing machines, notably those for blow moulding and injection moulding. It is therefore the most important single piece of equipment in the plastics industry.

Metal extrusion In this process a billet of material is forced under compression through an orifice which has a much smaller cross-section than that of the billet. The original process has been developed into a variety of loosely-related methods. Many of these are closely akin to FORGING although they are correctly described as extrusion. The best known process is *direct (solid)* extrusion. The billet, of squat cylindrical shape, is inserted into a strong steel container in which it fits quite closely. At the front end of the container is the die which contains one or more orifices to determine the cross-sectional shape of the extruded material and which, in the case of conventional forward extrusion, is fixed in relation to the container. The back end of the container is closed by a ram which moves forward to apply the extrusion force to the billet. The

metal is therefore forced through the die whereas in *reverse extrusion*, the die is not fixed to the container but is forced into the metal billet by the ram.

Extrusion was first used for the manufacture of lead pipe. When the process was later extended to metals of higher melting point it was developed as a hot working process, probably because it was thought that these harder materials had insufficient plasticity at room temperature. Thus, copperbase materials are commonly extruded at temperatures of about 700 to 900 °C (1290 to 1650 °F) while the corresponding figures for aluminium alloys are 400 to 550 °C (750 to 1020 °F). The hot extrusion of steel requires temperatures of 1100 to 1200 °C (2010 to 2190 °F) but these high temperatures are only made possible by the use of glass as a lubricant to protect the tools. It was later realized that cold extrusion of many hard materials is quite practicable provided a suitable press of sufficiently large capacity is available. The cold extrusion of difficult materials is facilitated by hydrostatic extrusion. In this process the billet is completely surrounded by a fluid which transmits the force from the ram hydrostatically, and also acts as a lubricant.

The required extrusion force is determined by the cross-

Below: a plastics extruder. The screws work on the archimedean principle inside a heated barrel. The polymer is fed in in granular form and is reduced to a homogeneous consistency as it melts in the heat generated from the friction and the heater bands. It is propelled forwards through three zones of feed, compression and metering and out through the die at the far end of the machine.

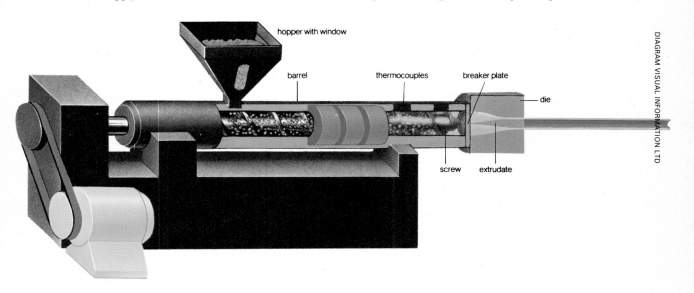

hopper with window

barrel   thermocouples   breaker plate   die

screw   extrudate

DIAGRAM VISUAL INFORMATION LTD

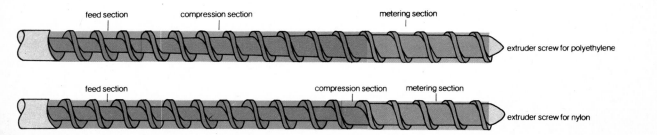

feed section   compression section   metering section

extruder screw for polyethylene

feed section   compression section   metering section

extruder screw for nylon

sectional area of the billet, the resistance to deformation of the material and the extrusion ratio. Large forces are required and presses have been constructed with capacities in excess of 1200 tons.

The extrusion ratio, obtained by dividing the cross-sectional area of the billet by that of the extruded section, varies from one material to another and may be as little as 5 or as much as 400. Thus, the process imposes considerable plastic deformation but unfortunately this is not always distributed very uniformly throughout the final extrusion. In the conventional hot process, the first foot or so of the extrusion to emerge from the die is substantially unaltered from the condition of the billet,

usually as cast, and must be rejected. Within the remainder of the extrusion there is a variation of deformation not only along the length but also across the cross-section and there are corresponding variations in structure and mechanical properties. The principal advantage of the process is that it can be used to produce a wide variety of cross-sections, both solid and hollow, ranging from simple circular and rectangular bars and wires to highly complex geometrical forms.

Plastic films are formed by extruding melted plastic either through a circular die and blowing head, or through a flat film die. In a circular die a tube is formed which is inflated with air and finally slit.

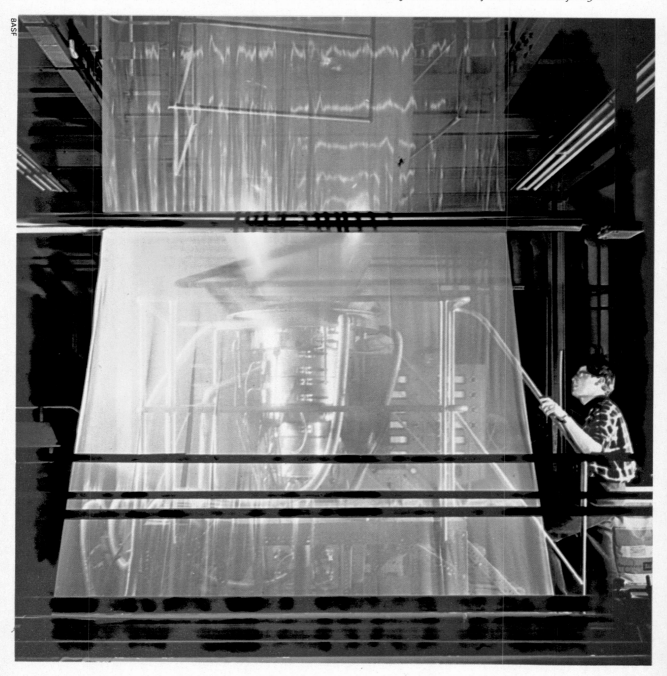

BASF

F

FABRIC

There are three main types of fabric: woven, knitted and *fibre*. The term fibre is used to describe the so-called non-woven fabrics, that is those not formed by WEAVING, which is the interlacement of two threads (warp threads which run lengthwise and weft threads which run across). Such fabrics are manufactured from a sheet, web or *batt* of either aligned or randomly orientated fibres that are held together usually by a combination of mechanical, chemical or solvent processes. For example, in one mechanical method, barbed needles punch into the web of fibres to entangle them thoroughly. A FELT is produced by the ability of certain fibres to mat together under the action of moisture, heat and pressure. The term non-woven is also used for fabrics where a web of fibres is held together by stitching threads or where one set of fibres is laid, non-interlaced, across another set and they are bound by a third set of threads knitting into them.

Many of the modern soft manmade fibres as well as woollen yarn lend themselves to knitted type fabrics. They are produced by a continuous thread interlacing or looping with itself as it traverses to and fro, or by a series of threads interlooping with adjacent threads (see KNITTING MACHINE).

Origins of woven fabrics

Although there are no records regarding the origin of weaving, Paleolithic man had undoubtedly acquired the arts of twisting cords, plaiting and sewing, while Neolithic man cultivated and used flax for woven structures.

Remains of flax threads, SPINNING whorls and weaver's weights, and remnants of woven cloths (some of them *twilled*) have been found in ancient Swiss lake dwellings, so there is evidence that during the later Stone Age mankind selected textile fibres and acquired the skills of spinning and weaving. The art of weaving was further developed by the early Egyptians. Fine linens have been discovered in their tombs, and LOOMS were depicted in wall paintings, for example at Thebes.

Simple woven fabric structures

Simple weaves are formed by the over and under interlacement of one series of threads (the *weft*) with another series of threads (the *warp*). In plain weaves the two series are at right angles to each other.

The simplest weaves are *plain*, *twill* (characterized by diagonal lines on the face of the fabric) and *satin*. The *mat* weaves are also simple but are really a derivation of plain weave, groups of threads being interlaced rather than a single thread.

Forty-five degree twill weaves are formed by interlacing each warp thread over and under a group of weft threads but they differ from mat weaves in that each interlacing moves one weft thread off compared with its neighbour, resulting in a diagonal pattern. This diagonal pattern can be upwards from right to left (S-twill) or upwards from left to right (Z-twill). Twill weaves may obviously be over or under to varying extents.

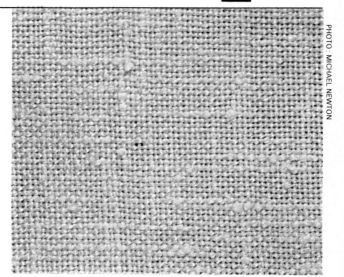

PHOTO: MICHAEL NEWTON

Top: simple weaves are formed by the under and over interlacement of one series of threads, the weft, over another series of threads, the warp. Shown here is the simplest form—plain weave with a single thread interlacement. There is a variation in thread thickness.

Bottom: another simple and very strong woven structure is the twill weave, which gives diagonal lines on the face of the fabric.

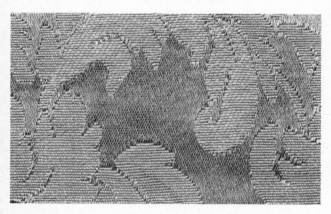

By moving the interlacings more than one thread off, the angle of twill can be varied. For example, 5–1–1–2–1–1 interlacings moved two off give the well-known *whipcord* weave, with a bold 5-float steep twill and the 1–1–2–1–1 part of the interlacings forming a sunken line between the bold twills. With simple twill weaves, however, variation of twill angle is arranged simply by arranging the thread spacing closer in one direction than the other such as in *gaberdine*.

Typical simple weaves where either the warp or the weft predominates on the face of the fabric include *satin* (warp dominated) and *sateen* (weft dominated). This is generally accentuated by the closer spacing of warp or weft respectively.

There are, however, two variations from the simple over and under interlacement of threads. In the first, *gauze* or *leno* structures, certain warp threads move alternately to right and left of adjacent threads between interlacements with the weft. The other is pile structures such as velvet, velveteens, corduroys, CARPETS and so on. In these there is the interlacing of weft with warp and base structure but additional threads are made to float or loop out from this base structure. If these long floats or loops are cut, a series of 'tufts' or cut pile result, but the loops may be left uncut as in terry towelling, uncut moquette and Brussels carpet.

Deep textures and compound structures   The interlacing of weft with warp can obviously be varied to an almost unlimited extent, allowing deep texture effects. In a honeycomb weave, for example, the more tightly interlacing threads 'sink' to a lower level in the woven fabric with the long floats of the more loosely interlacing threads rising to give the ridges a cellular effect. Texture may also be introduced by varying the yarn thickness.

Figuring in woven structures   Weave stripes, checks and figured designs are developed by combining two or more weave elements, either single or compound, in the total pattern of interlacing. Probably the best known stripe weave is the herringbone which alternates S and Z twills across the width of the fabric. Likewise the best known and commonest figured designs combine a warp predominant weave with a weft predominant weave. Extra threads are sometimes stitched to a ground structure so that the face effect is undisturbed but may be floated as required for some figure shape on the face.

Colour in woven structures   By introducing different coloured yarns throughout the warp and weft other design effects may be achieved. If the groups of coloured threads

Top: there are certain variations of the basic simple weaves which create quite a different structure. A marked textural effect is achieved in this leno type weave, where certain warp threads move alternately to the right and left of adjacent threads.

Next to top: pile and looped structures are other variations of simple weaves, where apart from the basic interlacement, additional threads are made to loop out to form the base structure as in towelling.

Next to the bottom: the most handsomely figured fabrics are the brocades. They are usually of single texture and the figure is developed by floating the warp threads or the weft threads, or sometimes both. The background is usually formed by a simple weave such as satin.

Bottom: possibly the best known traditional patterns are the tartans, formed by the use of coloured threads in the warp and weft. They evolved as a series of distinctive patterns for specific Scottish clans.

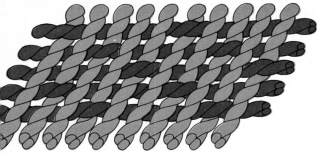

satin weave structure

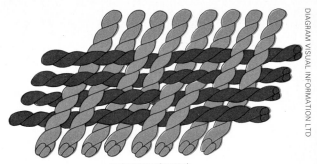

mat weave or hopsack

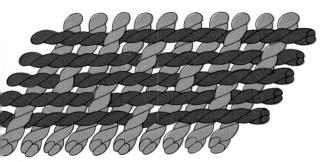

sateen weave structure

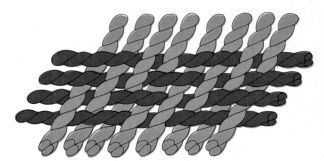

twill weave structure

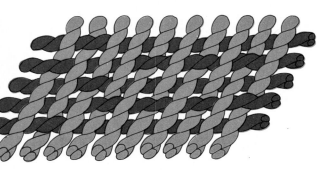

bedford cord

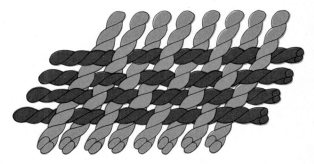

square sett, plain weave structure

p threads
rounded cords   weft threads   sunken lines between cords

rnate weft threads   warp over weft   weft over warp   **bedford cord**
t on back of cords

Above: 6 different types of fabric weave. In satin and sateen weaves either the weft or the warp predominates on the surface of the fabric. Twill weave, particularly used for woollen cloth, has a weft which passes first over and then under two warp threads. Hopsack has a rougher surface than the plain weave and bedford cord is made using a 'two-weft' structure.

Left: a point paper design for bedford cord. Crosses indicate warp over weft, oblique strokes alternate weft threads on the back of the cord, circles the sunken lines and blanks weft over warp.

are large, the emphasis is for coloured stripes and checks such as in the various tartans. If the thread groups are small, however, neither the colour pattern effect nor the weave is as apparent as the resulting effect of the different colour floats of warp and weft combining to give 'colour and weave' effects. These are virtually limitless in number and include various line, step, star and spot designs.

Fabric terms A few well known fabric terms are described here, but a more complete list is to be found in *Textile Terms and Definitions* published by the Textile Institute.

Brocade—a figured fabric, usually of single texture, in which the figure is developed by floating the warp threads, or the weft threads, or both, the threads being bound in a more or less irregular order. The ground is usually formed by a weave of simple elements. Many furnishing brocades are made with a satin ground and a weft figure. More elaborate fabrics are also made with more than one warp or weft or both.

Calico—a generic term for plain cotton cloth heavier than muslins.

Chiffon—originally a very light, sheer, open-mesh fabric made from silk yarns in plain weave; now also made from manmade fibre yarns. The term is loosely used adjectively to describe the lightest types of particular cloths such as 'chiffon velvets', and 'chiffon taffeta'.

Chintz—glazed, printed, plain-weave fabric, originally and usually of cotton and lighter than cretonne.

Crêpe—a fabric characterized by a crinkled or puckered surface. The effect may be produced in a variety of ways, for example, by the use of S and Z hard-twisted yarns, by the use of a crêpe weave, or by chemical treatment in finishing to produce differential shrinkage.

Crepon—a crêpe fabric more rugged that the average crêpe, with a fluted or crinkled effect in the warp direction.

Cretonne—a printed fabric originally and usually of cotton and of heavier weight than chintz.

Damask—a figured fabric made with one warp and one weft in which, generally, warp satin and weft sateen weaves interchange. Twill or other binding weaves may sometimes be introduced.

Denim—a cotton cloth in warp-faced twill made from yarn-dyed warp and undyed weft yarn.

Dimity—a fabric, usually cotton, that is checked or striped by corded effects which are made by weaving two or more threads as one.

Drill—a twill fabric of similar construction to a denim but usually piece-dyed.

Flannel—an all-wool fabric of plain or twill weave which feels soft. It may be slightly milled (processed so that the felting properties of the wool fibres make it impossible to see the weave) or raised (brushed to raise the nap).

Flannelette—a cloth made from cotton warp and soft-spun cotton weft, subsequently raised on both sides to give an imitation of the true flannel.

Georgette—a fine, light-weight, open texture fabric, usually in plain weave, made from crêpe yarns, usually two S-twisted and two Z-twisted in both warp and weft.

Jean—a 2–1 warp-faced twill fabric used chiefly for overalls. The term Jeanette is sometimes used to describe the lighter weight cloths, and these may be used for linings.

Muslin—a general term for a light weight, open cloth of plain weave or simple leno weave.

Seersucker—a fabric characterized by the presence of puckered and relatively flat sections, particularly in stripes but also in

A loom in a textile mill in Scotland set up ready for weaving with a soft mohair and wool yarn. Warp threads run down the fabric so must be reasonably strong and are therefore plied.

checks. The effect may be produced in a variety of ways, for example, by weaving so that ground warp threads are tensioned more than the puckered stripe threads, or by chemical treatment so that certain parts of the fabric contract more than others.

Serge—a piece-dyed fabric, of simple twill weave of square or nearly square construction, and with a clear finish.

Shantung—a plain-weave, silk dress fabric exhibiting random yarn irregularities resulting from the use of yarn spun from wild (Tussah) silk.

Taffeta—a plain-weave, closely-woven, smooth and crisp fabric with a faint weft-way rib, produced from filament yarns. The rib effect is due to the warp thread spacing being closer than the weft thread spacing. Taffeta belongs to a group of fabrics having ribs in the weft direction. Examples of the group, in ascending order of prominence of rib are: taffeta, poult, faille and grosgrain.

Tapestry—a closely-woven, figured fabric of compound structure in which the pattern is developed by the use of coloured yarns in the warp or weft or both; a fine binder warp may also be incorporated. It is normally used for upholstery. Originally the term was applied to furnishing fabrics in which the design was produced by coloured threads inserted by hand as required.

Zephyr—a fine cloth of plain weave used for dresses, blouses and shirtings and made in various qualities. A typical cotton zephyr has coloured stripes on a white ground and a cord effect made by the introduction of coarse threads at intervals.

FABRIC PRINTING

Fabric printing is now almost wholly mechanized, having been developed from methods such as block printing (which is similar in principle to printing from a lino-cut) or printing by means of a stencil. Probably the most common method is by means of rollers, the metal surfaces of which are engraved with the design. Each roller is 'furnished' with colour by means of a brush-covered furnishing roller which in turn dips into a trough of colour 'paste'. Surplus colour is scraped off the roller by an accurately ground *doctor blade*, leaving the colour in the recessed engraved design portions. The colour roller presses against the fabric, which passes over a large rotating cylinder. A second doctor blade scrapes off any fibrous impurity from the roller face before it is re-furnished with colour. A separate roller is required for each colour component of the design; thus an eight-colour print requires eight engraved rollers, which are expensive. The whole machine is of massive construction, and setting up the heavy rollers for a printing operation takes time. Accordingly, the method is most suitable for long printing runs of many thousands of yards or metres.

Screen printing In screen printing a stencil is developed photochemically on a strong fine-mesh material which has been stretched over a large rectangular frame. This material was originally of silk—hence the name silk-screen printing—but is now almost wholly of tougher materials such as nylon, polyester or metal. The screen lies on top of the cloth to be printed, the colour being forced through the open parts by a squeegee. In the manual system, now used only for speciality work, the cloth is stuck to a long table and the operators move the screen along—one screen for each colour component. In

Top: the Javanese word Batik is used for a wax resist method of dyeing fabric. Designs are produced on the cloth by covering all parts to be protected from the dye with wax in turn for each colour.

Bottom: hand silk screen printing at a textile mill in Bombay, India. The dye is forced through the holes in the screen by drawing a squeegee across it, a different screen being used for each colour.

the mechanical systems, the cloth is carried on an endless belt over a relatively short table; the screens are lowered, the printing stroke made, and the screens lifted to permit the cloth to move on the distance of one pattern repeat. Production is slower than by roller, but as the screens are cheaper to make and take less time to set up, the method is particularly suitable for relatively short runs. It will also permit wide design repeats, but is less suitable for unbroken patterns; for example it would be impossible to print a lengthwise stripe without visible overlapping joins.

Useful features of both systems are combined by using cylindrical screens, in which the screen is virtually a hollow roller with a fine mesh surface through which the colour, fed through the axle, is forced by means of an internal squeegee. The rate of production is higher than with flat screens, though the screens themselves are more expensive.

Dyes and pigments

Colours used in printing commonly comprise dye solutions 'thickened' to the consistency of a thin porridge by means of starches or gums. The product is a 'colour paste' and permits sharp outlines because the colour does not spread. After printing, the fabric is dried and the colour *fixed*, usually by passing through a large steam chamber. Some combinations of dye and fibre require high-pressure steam to fix them. Some dyes must be oxidized to obtain the correct shade, and the fabric must be thoroughly washed to remove the thickener together with surplus dye. These aftertreatments are of vital importance if proper colour values and fastness are to be obtained.

Pigment printing differs in that it utilizes a pigment which by itself would have no affinity for the fabric but which is applied along with a resin, firmly binding it to the fibre. Pigment and resin are thickened not with starches but with a spirit emulsion the consistency of thick cream. There is no inconvenient steaming or afterwash, a simple heat treatment,

Top: an automatic silk screen printing machine. The cloth is fed along under tension. The cloth stops, each screen prints its own colour and the cloth moves one screen along. The latest process is rotary screen printing, which is continuous and therefore faster.

Bottom left: a 'grid' for patterns for machine programmed film strip which is used for electronic scanning in automatic fabric printing.

Bottom right: dyes used in fabric printing are thickened to the consistency of paste to provide sharp outlines. The roller engraved with the design can be seen below and above it the 'furnishing' roller which transfers the thick dye to the recesses in the engraved roller. Excess dye is scraped off by the doctor blade. Accurate colour register is vital.

Right: fabric printing. The dye is taken up through the furnishing and continuous printing roller. The blanket, protected by the back grey, gives a greater resilience.

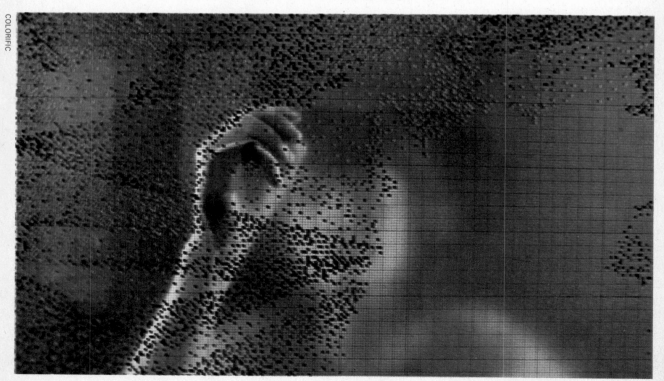

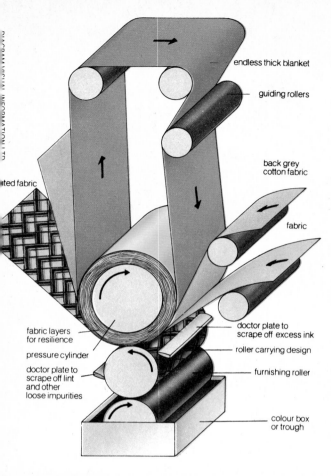

endless thick blanket

guiding rollers

back grey
cotton fabric

...ted fabric

fabric

fabric layers
for resilience

pressure cylinder

doctor plate to
scrape off lint
and other
loose impurities

doctor plate to
scrape off excess ink

roller carrying design

furnishing roller

colour box
or trough

for example four minutes at 130°C (266°F), being all that is required. The method is not, however, suitable for all types of fabric.

As well as applying colour in the form of a pattern (the *direct* style) it is possible to produce patterns removing the colour from fabric which has previously been dyed in the conventional way. By printing with a paste containing an appropriate chemical, the dye is destroyed. This is the *discharge* style and can be elaborated by including in the discharge paste a different type of dye which is unaffected by the chemical, and which is thus substituted for the original colour. In the *resist* style the fabric is printed with a chemical which prevents uptake of dye during subsequent dyeing; by incorporating a different type of dye in the resist paste a coloured resist is obtained. Discharge and resist styles are less used than formerly.

Transfer printing The newest method, which though forming only a small fraction of total printwork is expanding rapidly, is that of *transfer* printing. Paper, which because of its rigidity and smooth surface can be roller printed very accurately, is printed with a type of dye which vaporizes when strongly heated to approximately 200°C (390°F). If this paper is then passed through an accurately controlled hot press along with the textile fabric, dye transfer takes place. No aftertreatment is necessary and there are fewer problems with fine non-absorbent fabrics which are difficult to print conventionally. Some limitations arise in respect of dye fastness, and only fabrics made from fibres capable of being dyed with this particular type of dye can be printed in this way. The 'messy' part of printing now becomes the province of the paper printer, who holds large stocks of designs which can be supplied at very short notice to the textile processer, who in turn needs the very minimum of space and equipment. Considerable research is being directed to extending this method to a wider range of fabrics.

FACSIMILE TRANSMISSION

The word facsimile comes from the Latin for 'to make the same', and facsimile transmission involves using one machine, the *transmitter*, to scan a document and convert the image into electrical impulses, which are then transmitted by TELEPHONE cable or radio link to a second machine, the *receiver*. This machine uses these impulses to create an exact likeness of the original document.

The first facsimile machine was invented by a Scotsman, Alexander Bain, in 1842. It was a crude device by modern standards, using a pendulum fitted with a stylus to carve an image on to a metal surface coated with shellac (a yellow natural resin secreted by the lac insect and used for varnishes and insulating films). More recently, facsimile transmission (often called *fax transmission*) has been developed into a reliable system giving a high quality of reproduction, which can now compete with the more established forms of communication such as post, TELEPRINTER and Telex services.

The transmitter The most widely used system uses a transmitter and receiver linked by ordinary telephone lines. This is an advantage in that a fax transmitter can be installed wherever a telephone line is available, but one drawback is that telephone equipment is designed for speech transmission, and its frequency range is therefore somewhat limited. Speech consists of sound waves within the approximate range of 300

to 3400 Hz, and telephone equipment is designed accordingly. This means that fax equipment must produce its image signals within that range to make best use of the telephone system, because any signals outside of that frequency band would be distorted, with a corresponding loss of copy quality.

The document to be transmitted is loaded into the machine where it is read (scanned) by a PHOTOELECTRIC detector, which converts the image on the paper into an electrical signal. The document may be wrapped around a cylinder which rotates as it moves past the scanner, or else kept flat and moved past the scanner which reads across it as it passes (the *flat bed* type).

A light is shone on the document, and the signal produced by the detector is proportional to the amount of light which is reflected on to it from the paper. White areas give a lot of reflection, black areas none at all, and shades of grey vary in between these two. The signal from the detector is amplified and then modulated (either by AMPLITUDE MODULATION or FREQUENCY MODULATION) to produce an audio frequency signal which can be transmitted by radio or telephone.

The receiver The receiver works on either the cylinder or flat bed principle, according to the type of transmitter used, and there are several different ways in which the transmitted image can be recorded on paper. In every case, however, the incoming signal is first *demodulated* to give a fluctuating signal corresponding to that produced by the detector in the transmitter. This signal is then used to drive the recording system after passing through a *driver* amplifier.

For high quality transmission of photographs (for newspaper use, for instance) the image may be recorded optically on photographic film, which is then developed in the normal way. Other systems use a variety of methods to reproduce the image,

Below : diagram illustrating the operation of a rotating drum type facsimile transmission system. The transmitter, on the left, reads the document by means of the photocell arrangement, and the signal is transmitted to the receiving machine which produces the copy by burning away the top coating of the electroresistive paper.

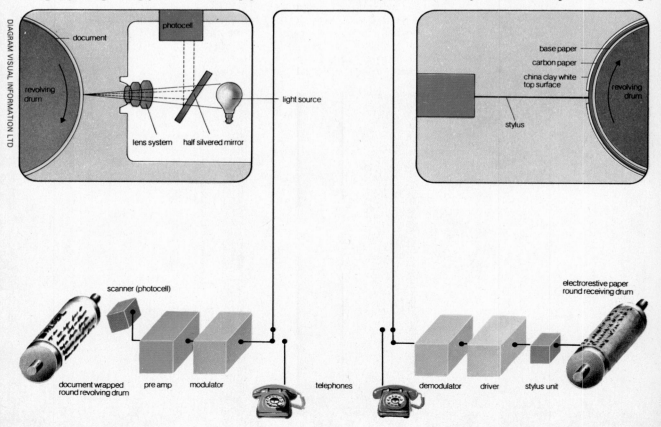

including *thermal*, *electrolytic*, ELECTROSTATIC, and *percussive* techniques. Before the copy transmission begins, *phasing* signals are transmitted to synchronize the receiver with the transmitter.

The thermal systems use *electroresistive* paper, which is made up of three layers: a base paper, a carbon layer in the middle, and a top coating of white CHINA CLAY. The output from the driver is fed to a moving stylus which rests on the paper. When the transmitter 'sees' a black area on the original document, the signal produced by the photocell is at a minimum, and when it sees a white area the signal is at a maximum. The system *inverts* these signal levels so that when a black area is read by the transmitter the current fed to the stylus is at a maximum. The current flows through the stylus and along the carbon layer in the paper, burning away the white top coating of the paper immediately under the stylus, exposing the black carbon layer beneath it. The circuit is completed by a contact between the carbon layer and the drum or bed of the machine.

When the transmitter reads a white area, the signal in the photocell is at a maximum and the current in the stylus at a minimum, and so the fax copy is left white. Grey shades produce intermediate current levels resulting in only partial burning of the white coating.

The electrostatic machines work in a similar way to electrostatic copiers: the black areas of the original are reproduced as electrostatically charged areas on the copy paper. These charged areas attract a dry, black powder which produces the image.

The percussive system uses an overlay of carbon paper above the copy paper. Signals from the transmitter drive a stylus against the carbon paper to produce the image on the copy paper.

Another type of receiver uses an electrolytic process, creating the image by the ELECTROLYSIS of an electrolyte impregnated into the paper. The electrodes are two wires, a straight one in front of the paper and one wrapped helically around a rotating drum behind it. The paper moves along between the electrodes to give one direction of scan, and the intersection between the straight wire and the rotating helical wire moves across the paper as the drum rotates, providing the other direction of scan. Dark areas of the copy are produced by passing a current between the electrodes to discolour the paper, either by a chemical change in the electrolyte or by electrolytic action on the fixed electrode which leaves a deposit on the paper.

Applications

All facsimile transmission equipment must comply with the stringent regulations laid down by the International Telegraph and Telephone Consultative Committee, which ensure that the machines are safe for the operators to use and are suitable for use on the telephone network.

Facsimile transmission has been used for a long time by newspapers and press agencies. The business applications are comparatively recent, but are increasing rapidly as a wider range of reliable, low cost equipment becomes available. As an alternative to the postal system, fax transmission is faster and there is no risk of the document being lost in transit. Telex is faster, but the print quality of letters is low and pictures or diagrams cannot be sent at all. As the original document is used, the facsimile is an exact copy and there is no problem with errors caused by inaccurate typing.

Using a radio link, facsimile copies may be sent to vehicles, ships and aircraft, and this system is also used by weather satellites to transmit pictures of cloud formations to ground stations. Facsimile transmission of weather maps and information has been used by the US Army and Air Force for over thirty years.

Many police authorities now use fax systems to transmit information on known criminals, including fingerprints which are first enlarged by using a POLAROID CAMERA.

In Austria a fax network has been established to enable deaf and dumb people to communicate, using normal telephone connections.

So far, only monochrome facsimile transmission is possible, but colour systems are being developed, as are machines which can be loaded with a stack of papers and left to contact the receiving station automatically, check that the receiver is ready, and then transmit the documents one by one.

Above: this facsimile machine uses a stylus to apply a negative charge to the areas of the copy paper to be darkened. The paper is then treated with a positively charged dye, which dyes only the charged areas.

Left: news pictures are often sent by wire. The vertical lines are caused by electrical faults on the telephone line.

FAIRGROUND MACHINES

Fairs were originally annual gatherings of people living in scattered rural communities, offering an opportunity for them to meet, barter and buy goods that would not normally reach them. These events became the occasions for various entertainments, among which would have been small roundabouts or merry-go-rounds in which the children sat on donkeys moving in a circle. With the coming of steam power, these were replaced by faster and larger mechanical devices, *carousels*, which adults could ride on as well.

The first carousels were operated by steam traction engines, which used steam to drive a large flywheel. This was connected by a belt to the centre of the merry-go-round, while some of the steam was used to play a steam organ.

Instead of real donkeys, the carousel has model horses on poles extending from the base platform to the overhead canopy. These are attached at the top to a crank operated by a bevel gear from the central crown wheel so that as the whole thing rotates the 'animals' move up and down. The movements are arranged to balance each other such that at any one time as many horses are moving upwards as downwards, so as not to put an irregular load on the drive mechanism.

As electricity came into use, the traction engine was made to drive DC generators, first for lighting the ride and then for driving it directly, so that the generator could be kept well away from the ride. Eventually DIESEL ENGINES replaced the traction engine completely, and are the rule in modern travelling fairgrounds. They drive DC generators, commonly of 110 volt output, since direct current ELECTRIC MOTORS can be controlled over a large speed range by using a simple rheostat or resistance coil. These have to handle a large load when the motor is running at low speed, so in their simplest form consist of several feet of wound copper bands with a sliding contact.

A typical fairground ride may need 15 to 25 hp (11 to 19 kW) for the rotary motion. Because of the heavy load placed on the generator when the ride starts, it is usual to run the lighting and sound systems off another generator so that the lights do not dim and the music does not slow down or fade away.

Types of ride Travelling fairground rides usually provide simple variations on the merry-go-round principle. The 'caterpillar', for example, has cars running round a circular undulating track, moved by arms extending from a central shaft. Around this shaft is a sleeve with cables attached to it: these cables connect to an awning which can be pulled over the cars completely. When the ride is in motion, the sleeve is stopped

Left: this is Sir Hiram Maxim's Flying Machine, built in 1903 and still in daily use at Blackpool Pleasure Beach, England. Though the cabins are new, the machinery (below left) is Maxim's original—he was famous for the first automatic machine gun and for a steam-powered aircraft experiment in 1894. Two 50 hp (37 kW) DC motors are linked by rope drives to 12 foot (3.6 m) diameter wheels, one of which can be seen on the right of the picture. These in turn drive the bevel gears which turn the crown wheel attached to the central column. On this column can be seen some of the slip rings which transfer electric current to the ride for lighting. Even the manila ropes which link the motors to the drive wheels are themselves quite hard-wearing—they last had to be replaced over 25 years ago.

Below: the moving chain drive which pulls cars up the slope of a gravity ride. Alongside the chain is a simple but effective safety device—a ratchet in which a pawl may catch if the cars should begin to move backwards. The framework for these rides, which may be built to considerable heights, is made of timber which can be used in long lengths, such as American Long Leaf Pitch Pine.

relative to the central pivot so that the cables wind up on it, pulling the awning over the cars to the amusement of their occupants.

Another common ride is the 'whip'. In this, cars are carried round a track on the end of arms and are free to pivot on the ends of these arms. The track is elliptical or oval, and the cars obey KEPLER's laws just as the planets of the solar system do. They have to move faster around the sharp curves than they do round the straight parts of the track, so they swing violently back and forth on their pivots, which travel at a constant rate.

The 'chairoplane' has chairs or cabins hanging on the ends of cables, so that they are free to swing out by centrifugal force as the machine turns. A modern variation on this has rocket-shaped cabins on arms which rotate from a central hub. These arms can be raised or lowered by compressed air cylinders controlled from the cabin by the passengers. The air comes from a separate compressor and is carried by a rotating knuckle joint with 'O' rings at the centre of the hub. When the ride is over, the operator lets the air out of the system by a central valve, so that all the cabins are brought down to ground level. If air pressure fails for some reason, the same thing will happen; the tubing used in the system is of sufficiently small bore to let the cabins down gently.

Below: the underneath of a gravity ride car. Projecting underneath are the safety pawl (right) and the dog which engages in the chain. As well as the two rails which the cars run on, there are four others which restrain the movement of the cars in all other sideways and up-and-down directions, as shown here.

Right: the layout of the Whip involves an oval track, of which one end is seen here. A cable passes round two wheels which provide the operating power, and the cars are attached to the cable by bars with spring shock absorbers to prevent violent jerks.

Below right: this is the underneath of a large amusement park version of the carousel, the Derby Racer at Blackpool. 56 horses rotate with a 50 ton platform driven by a 50 hp (37 kW) motor via a cable which passes right round it. Each horse rides on an undulating track below the platform, shown here. At the same time, another cable attached to each horse and passing round a series of pulleys moves the horses back and forth in a slot, adding yet another motion to the ride. There are over 1000 greasing points to be maintained.

A wide variation of rides can be produced using combinations of these techniques, with cranks, CAMS and eccentric arms to produce the irregular motions. Fairground engineers prefer mechanical rather than electronic solutions to problems, since mechanical devices are more robust and easily maintained.

Other rides One amusement which does not use rotary motion is the 'dodgem cars'. These derive electric power from the overhead wire mesh through a sliding contact strip; their operating area has a metal floor, completing the circuit. This floor is maintained at earth potential, so that people do not get electric shocks as they step on to it. The cars have $\frac{1}{2}$ hp (375 watt) motors, using just a few amps of current at 110 volts DC. This is not enough to cause much heating of the wire mesh or the contact strip, but by gearing of the motor it provides enough power for the motion. The motor turns with the steering; it drives the front wheel of the three wheeled vehicles. The steering can turn through over 180°, to allow great manoeuvrability. Because dodgem cars often get stuck, an automatic clutch mechanism disconnects the motor drive from the wheel if the load on it is too great, so protecting the motor.

The 'roller coaster' is known as a *gravity ride*: after the cars have been hauled to the top of their track, the rest of the ride takes place by the force of gravity. The tracks are designed with

undulations so that the cars just have sufficient force after swooping downwards to make it to the top of the next hill.

There are a number of ways of hauling the cars to the top of the hills: one well-tried method has a heavy duty CHAIN DRIVE continuously operating up the slope. A lug or *dog* under the car engages in one link of this chain, there being several dogs for each train of cars so that if one fails, another will take over. As a further safety device, there is a ratchet (set of teeth) on the track up the slope, in which a pawl under the car can engage if anything goes wrong. There is also a flange projecting beneath the cars, which can be gripped by pairs of boards to brake the cars either in an emergency or at the end of the ride.

Roller coasters are more common in permanent amusement parks, in view of their size. The permanent parks usually have a rather greater variety of rides and amusements than the travelling fairgrounds can offer, such as water rides. One such device is adapted from the timber industry's technique of transporting logs on rapid water flows or *log flumes*. Log shaped vessels are carried along by the water, with occasional ramps rather like those of the roller coaster to lift the boats out of the water and let them slide down again to rejoin the water with a splash.

A permanent amusement park will be more likely to use mains AC electricity rather than DC where possible, for convenience of supply. Modern hydraulic motors are much more compact than electric motors, and can produce high speed and good power application. They consist of turbines operating on hydraulic fluid at pressure; the pressure is provided by rotary pumps, and may be as high as 3000 psi (200 bar). These run continuously, and the pressure is applied to the motor progressively by means of a valve to speed up the ride.

FARAD (see capacitance)

FARADAY, Michael (1791–1867)

Michael Faraday is best known for a brilliant series of experiments on the nature of ELECTRICITY which resulted in the invention of the DYNAMO and the formation of his laws of ELECTROLYSIS (the breakdown of solutions by electricity).

Faraday was born in Newington Butts, Surrey, on 22 November 1791, and was the son of a blacksmith. He became interested in science when he attended some lectures given in 1812 by Sir Humphrey DAVY. After serving an apprenticeship in bookbinding, he sent his lecture notes to Davy, along with a request for a job. In 1813 he began work as Davy's assistant at the Royal Institution; later that year he accompanied Davy on a European tour, which was good experience for the modestly educated young scientist. Persistent conflict with Lady Davy, however, made the journey an ordeal.

After his return to the Royal Institution, Faraday had to work hard, since he was the main source of income for the Institution, which was then having financial difficulties. During this period Faraday worked on glass and steel, performed many chemical analyses and investigated the chlorides of carbon for Davy. His work resulted in the discovery of benzene in 1825.

Davy had by then left the Institution, but Faraday had been

Below left: rotors spin at about 17 rpm, pressing their occupants to a nearly vertical cage through centrifugal force.

Below: the original ring used by Michael Faraday in his experiment of 1831 to demonstrate the phenomenon of electromagnetic induction. Two coils of wire were wound on the same ring of iron and a voltage applied across one coil, inducing a voltage across the other.

Right: Michael Faraday lecturing at the Royal Institution before the Prince Consort (1855). His experiments and lectures covered many subjects including the chemistry of carbon and properties of gases.

ZEFA

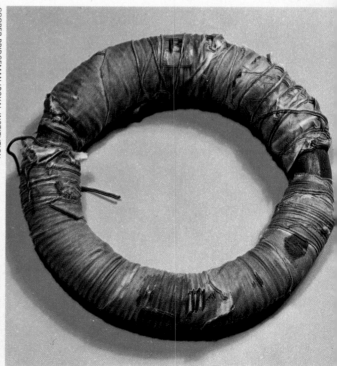

COOPER BRIDGEMAN / ROYAL INSTITUTION

much influenced by him and performed many experiments for him. When Faraday discovered, in 1823, that gases could be liquefied by pressure, Davy took the credit. Later the two were in conflict when Davy opposed the election of Faraday as a fellow of the Royal Society; it seemed that Davy was jealous of the younger man.

In 1821, the year he married, Faraday was asked by a scientific journal to write an article about the new electrical phenomena. There were many isolated discoveries at that time which defied explanation. For example, OERSTED had noticed that a wire carrying current affects a compass needle. Faraday realized that a magnet would push a wire to one side, and devised an experiment to demonstrate it. He suspended a wire carrying current over a magnet, and found that it moved in circles around the magnet. This experiment made him famous throughout Europe, but led to some false charges of plagiarism.

By 1831 the Royal Institution was in better financial condition, and Faraday was able to concentrate on research. In that year he performed his famous ring experiment demonstrating electromagnetic INDUCTION. It followed from his idea of what caused the wire to move in a magnetic field, and he had been trying to demonstrate the effect since 1821. When a current flowing through a coil of wire on one side of an iron ring was switched on or off, it induced a current in a coil on the other side. He reasoned that a 'magnetic wave' was produced by the first coil and passed through the second, causing an electric current to flow. A way of sustaining the wave was to rotate the conductor (a copper disc) in a magnetic field; in doing so, Faraday had constructed the first dynamo.

In the next few years, by passing currents through solutions, Faraday showed that all kinds of electricity, however generated, were the same. In this way he developed his laws of electrolysis, which relate the amount of decomposition in a solution to the amount of current passed through it.

In 1839 Faraday suffered a mental breakdown; his convalescence, in England and abroad, took four years. His breakdown left him with a poor memory, which grew worse with time. He returned to his work, this time investigating the effect of a magnetic field on non-metallic substances. These are weakly attracted or repelled, and Faraday introduced the names *paramagnetic* and *diamagnetic* for them. His scientific work began to suffer at the expense of his dabbling in other, less demanding activities. In 1853 Faraday investigated 'table-turning', in which supernatural forces were supposed to be at work. Two years later he wrote a letter to *The Times* about water pollution in the Thames.

Tragically, in the late 1850s he began to find lecturing more difficult. Lecturing was a love of Faraday's; he had carefully observed Davy as a young man and took much care with his own lectures. Ironically, it was during this period that he delivered his most famous lectures, including *The Chemical History of the Candle*.

In 1861 Faraday, then 70, retired from the Royal Institute and moved to a house in Hampton Court that Queen Victoria had offered him. By now his condition was so bad that he required permanent assistance. On 25 August 1867, he died, and was given a private funeral at Highgate Cemetery.

Faraday was able to blend theory and experiment in his researches to an extent few men have been able to match. He had little money to spend on apparatus and knew no mathematics. Many of his discoveries were not put to use until decades after his death. Perhaps his most important accomplishment was his research into electromagnetics, which was to be the seed of one of the major achievements of nineteenth century science: the development of FIELD theory by James MAXWELL.

FAUCET (see valve)

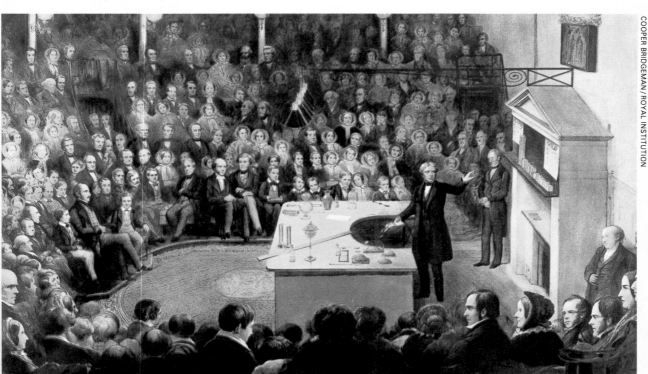

FEEDBACK

Feedback is encountered in systems and devices which have an input into them, and an output resulting from this, part of which is taken back to the input to modify this in some way. When one part of a multi-stage process is coupled to an earlier stage in the same process, a *feedback loop* is established, which can be used to monitor the process and make any adjustment that may be necessary.

Although of great importance in engineering systems and electronic circuits in particular, feedback is a word commonly used in social contexts to indicate this process of *readjustment*. For example, a broadcasting company may obtain 'feedback' from viewers or listeners on a programme it has transmitted which will affect the nature of future broadcasts. Also, a teacher obtains feedback from the children on teaching methods employed and may modify the curriculum accordingly. Consequently, feedback is an essential feature of teaching machines (see AUDIO VISUAL AIDS) where the pupil must be informed of his progress.

A simple feedback mechanism
A thermostatically controlled heater is a simple feedback system used to control the temperature of the room to a predetermined level set on the THERMOSTAT; the thermostat turns the heater off. The room then cools down and at a given temperature the thermostat turns the heater back on again and so on, maintaining the room temperature within required limits.

The feedback loop in this situation is provided by the hot air travelling from the heater to the thermostat and the thermostat connection to the switch controlling the fuel input to the heater.

Feedback in amplifiers
Feedback provides an extremely easy technique for controlling the gain (degree of amplification) of an electronic AMPLIFIER without altering any elements of the amplifier itself.

The amplifier alone has a certain fixed gain, called the *open loop gain* (open loop because there is no connection from the output to the input). This is the ratio of the output amplitude to the input amplitude which caused it.

When feedback is applied, a closed loop is created (from input to output back to input again). The feedback path includes an element which will allow only a certain fraction of the output amplitude back to the input. By controlling the size of this fraction, the feedback, and hence the closed loop gain of the system, can be controlled.

Positive and negative feedback
When the feedback signal is subtracted from the original input signal, the resulting type of feedback is negative. Negative feedback systems are inherently stable because any increase in the input signal is automatically counteracted by the returning (negative) feedback signal. The closed loop gain of such a system is therefore always less than the original open loop (no feedback) gain of the amplifier. By controlling the fraction of output to reach the input, this closed loop gain can be controlled.

With positive feedback the feedback signal is added to the original input signal. In such systems, the gain can be increased beyond the open loop value. This is because the feedback signal increases the total input signal to the amplifier and a correspondingly larger output signal results.

There is, however, a limit to which the gain can be increased before the system becomes unstable. When the fraction of output reaching the input is the reciprocal of the open loop amplifier gain (as 1/6 is the reciprocal of 6), the system 'lifts itself by its own bootstraps'. The output careers out of control from

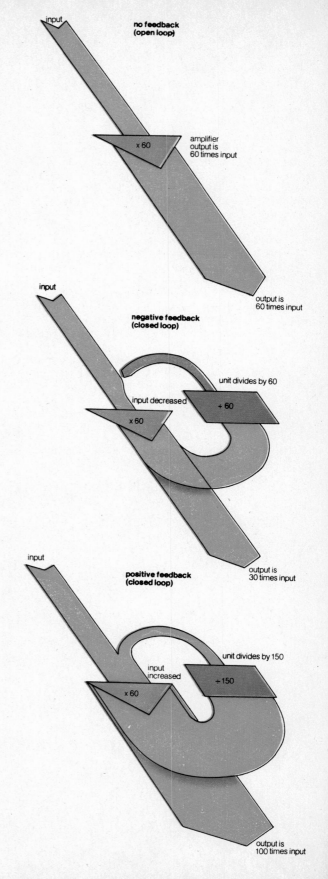

input
no feedback
(open loop)
x 60
amplifier output is 60 times input
output is 60 times input

input
negative feedback
(closed loop)
unit divides by 60
input decreased
÷ 60
x 60
output is 30 times input

input
positive feedback
(closed loop)
unit divides by 150
input increased
÷ 150
x 60
output is 100 times input

the size of the feedback signal alone and no input signal is necessary. The system becomes unstable and oscillations occur —this is the principle of the OSCILLATOR.

Feedback theory played an important part in the development of radio for this very reason. Before 1913 high frequency alternating voltages necessary for radio transmissions were impossible because ALTERNATORS could not be driven at the required high speeds. Positive feedback applied to the triode valve amplifier eventually overcame this problem and enabled medium and short wave frequencies to be used.

Other applications   The idea of using the results, or intermediate effects, of any process as a means of monitoring the process's efficiency is central nowadays to most branches of science and technology. 'Feedback' in this broadened sense is now commonly employed in such diverse areas as psychology, surgical anaesthetics, automation and, in particular, cybernetics and information theory. The term can now be used to describe any regulator or, in the case of totally automated devices such

Left: the open loop (no feedback) amplifier at top has a gain of 60. With negative feedback (middle), 1/60 of the output is subtracted from the input signal and the overall gain of the system is only 30 (even with amplifier gain 60). With positive feedback (bottom) 1/150 of the output is added to the input and the overall gain is 100.

as the steering controls of a heat-seeking missile or a computer-controlled assembly line, self-regulatory action. Feedback ranges in complexity from the reading of a pressure gauge by a human operator and the adjustments that he makes according to those readings, to the continuous corrections to the course of an aircraft made by an automatic pilot mechanism. Here, the instantaneous course and position are fed back into an electronic device which compares them to a reference course and position as given by the line of a radio signal. Any discrepancy between the actual and ideal values activates the aircraft's steering mechanism to reduce this difference.

The many types of SERVOMECHANISM that are widely used in the automatic regulation of processes play an important part in the technology of feedback control. A servomechanism is a device that responds to the discrepancy between the actual value of a variable, especially the position of an object, and the predetermined ideal value of position. This deviation, such as the difference between the actual position of a ship's compass needle and the position corresponding to a preset course, is almost invariably expressed as a small electrical current. This current is subsequently amplified, and then triggers an appropriate self-correcting response. This method is used, for example, to fire a small rocket which alters the course of a satellite in orbit.

FELT manufacture

Felt is one of the oldest fabrics, and the first woollen cloth may have been a form of felt made by the nomadic tribes of central Asia and Mongolia. It was widely used by the Romans and Greeks, and today has many applications ranging from clothing to specialized industrial felts.

Many types of fibrous material are used in felt making, including wool, cotton, jute, fur, hair, asbestos, and manmade fibres such as rayon, nylon and GLASS FIBRE. The final stages of the manufacture of these felts depend on the base materials and the type of felt being produced, but the initial stages are broadly similar to those described below, which apply more specifically to flooring, furnishing and insulating felts, which can be divided into *loose felts* and *needle punched felts*.

Loose felts are used as a filling for mattresses and cushions by the furnishing trade. Needle punched felts are used as carpet underfelts and for surrounding the interior spring units of mattresses. In sheet form, needle punched felt is used for insulating domestic water tanks, and in strip or tube form it can be used for pipe insulation.

Teasing   The raw materials are first blended in the correct proportions to produce the type of felt required. Underfelts are made from the surplus or waste yarns from the jute and carpet industries and loose felts from reclaimed waste from cloth weaving. These yarns and wastes must be *teased* (opened up) to form a fluffy mixture of separate fibres, which can then be processed.

This opening up of the fibres is carried out by holding the mixture of twisted yarns or wastes against a rapidly revolving cylinder on which there are thousands of hardened steel pins which separate the fibres by a high speed combing action. The opened fibres are now ready to be formed into a pad or *batt* of the required thickness and this can be achieved in two

Left: the first stage in the manufacture of felt is the blending of the fibres into the correct proportions by weight. Materials used include wool, jute, animal hair, and synthetic fibres, the choice of materials being determined by the type of felt required.

ways. The first is *carded* or *oriented web forming*, and the second is *random* or *air layering* (non-oriented web forming).

Carding

Carding is done on a machine which is in effect a mechanical comb consisting of one or more main cylinders (*swifts*) surrounded by a series of rollers revolving in different directions to give a combing action. The swifts and rollers are covered with a wire that has a saw-toothed edge. The fibres are fed in between the swifts and the rollers, and the resulting thin web of parallel fibres, whose mechanical strength is greatest in the direction in which the fibres lie, is then built up into layers. Each layer is placed so that the direction of the fibres is at an angle to the one below. This gives a reasonably strong batt, which is passed through compression rollers to produce a loose, bulky material which may be further processed by needle punching.

Random webbing

This is done on a machine similar to the teasing plant, which separates the fibres further, and has a suction hood set above the main rollers which draws the fibres up off the cylinder and allows them to fall like snow on to a moving apron whose speed can be altered as required, thus permitting a suitable batt to be built up. This batt is pressed under a consolidating roller to give an even pad which has a uniform mechanical strength in all directions and is not subject to peeling of the layers, as is the carded batt.

Needle punching

The batt formed by either of the above methods has no great mechanical strength and breaks easily if handled. It can be made stronger and firmer if some of the fibres are turned down through 90° from the general line interlocked with other fibres.

This is done by passing the batt through a needle loom, consisting of one or more laminated wood or alloy boards in which anything from a few hundred to several thousand needles are set.

The fibrous batt is laid on to a *scrim* (canvas or hessian backing sheet) and the batt and scrim are passed between two perforated steel sheets. The needles pass through these holes and through the batt, and are then withdrawn to allow the batt to move forward so that the next section can be punched.

The flow of material through the loom is controlled by varying the speed of the input and output rollers, and the forward motion is interrupted intermittently to allow the needles to penetrate and withdraw from the batt.

This produces a felt suitable for the bedding and furniture trades, but as a carpet underlay needs a much greater mechanical strength to stop it from spreading or creeping, a polypropylene scrim is used and the fibres are bonded not only to themselves but also to the scrim, providing high mechanical strength.

The degree of resilience of a carpet underlay can be altered by changing the number of punches, the gauge of the needles used, the speed of the material flow through the loom, or a combination of these factors. The final stage is to trim the edges with rotary knives, and cut the felt into the required length and width.

Other felts

After the carding or random webbing processes, there are many ways in which the batts can be treated to produce a felt, depending on the type required. These processes may involve moistening, steaming, rolling, and *fulling* (treating with a soap or acid solution), often followed by a dyeing process. Among the other main types of felt are the soft felts for the clothing industry, hard industrial felts for bearing seals, mounting blocks and insulating sheets, and woven felts such as those used in papermaking to convey and dry the wet 'slurry'.

BURY & MASCO INDUSTRIES LTD

Above left: part of a carding engine which produces the thin webs of fibres that are built up in layers to make the batts.

Above right: after the batt has been built up it is wound into rolls for further processing.

Right: the roller hardening machine uses steam, pressure and vibration to make pressed wool felt from the rolls of carded fibre. Wool fibres have a scaly surface, and it is this factor, together with the shrinkage properties of wool, that enables the fibres to interlock and matt together to form a felt. After the roller hardening process the felt is subjected to more heavy pounding in a milling machine which compacts the fibres even closer. The resulting felt is stretched and dried in a heated chamber, the loose surface hairs are removed, and the felt is given a final pressing. Wool felt is naturally white or grey, but can easily be dyed in a large range of colours.

BURY & MASCO INDUSTRIES LTD

BURY & MASCO INDUSTRIES LTD

FERMI, Enrico (1901–1954)

'The Italian navigator has landed in the New World', was the cryptic message that went out on the afternoon of 2 December 1942, to announce the successful operation of the world's first nuclear reaction. Enrico Fermi, the Christopher Columbus of atomic energy, had simply smiled in satisfaction and said to his colleagues: 'The chain reaction has begun.'

Fermi's brilliance in physics was early apparent. Before he was 21 he had been awarded his physics PhD by the University of Pisa. Fermi was born in Rome but in 1944 became an American citizen. He grew up in a turbulent time for physics, when RELATIVITY and the QUANTUM THEORY were sweeping aside classical ideas.

Fermi first made major advances in atomic study by using the so-called exclusion principle of Wolfgang Pauli to explain how the particles of a gas behave at low temperatures and high densities, where they no longer obey the classical GAS LAWS. Such a *degenerate* gas (now also known as a Fermi gas) has properties like a metal, and indeed the electrons in a metal behave like a Fermi gas. Particles that follow the law he formulated are termed *fermions*.

In 1933 Fermi gave the name *neutrino*, meaning 'little neutral one', to a particle he predicted must be produced when a neutron decays into a proton and an electron. In this process, known as *beta decay*, the electron seems to be emitted with too little energy. Fermi supposed that a neutrino was also formed during the decay and carried away some of this energy. These ghostlike particles, which lack both mass and electrical charge, were detected experimentally in 1955.

In 1934, Irene and Frederic Joliot-Curie announced that radioactivity could be induced in some atoms by bombarding them with protons. Fermi sent one of his assistants out with a bag to visit chemical suppliers in Rome, saying: 'Get all the elements in Mendeleev's table if you can.' (Mendeleev's PERIODIC TABLE is the complete list of chemical ELEMENTS.) His team began to work their way through the periodic table, bombarding the atoms with neutrons, which Fermi reasoned would be easier for atomic nuclei to capture because they had no electric charge. Within two months, the Fermi team had produced several new radioactive isotopes.

During this work came the accidental discovery that a screen between the neutron source and the target actually increased the effect of the neutrons. This puzzling result was particularly marked when solid paraffin (wax) was used as a screen. Over lunch, Fermi had a flash of insight: perhaps the hydrogen nuclei in the paraffin were slowing the neutrons so that they became easier to capture. To test the theory, the group decided to see if water (which also contains hydrogen) would produce the same result. Passing their neutrons through a nearby goldfish pond, the team were able to confirm Fermi's hunch.

But the group remained puzzled by the results of bombarding uranium. Several decay products were formed, but they could not identify them. Though no one knew it at the time, this work contained the key that opened the door to the atomic reactor.

Fermi was awarded the physics Nobel prize in 1938 for his work in producing new radioactive substances and discovering the importance of slow neutrons. He never returned to Italy after collecting the prize in Stockholm. Fermi did not agree with the Fascist government at home, and racial laws threatened his Jewish wife. So they sailed on to the United States, where Fermi obtained a post at Columbia University in 1939.

Meanwhile, Otto Hahn and Fritz Strassmann in Berlin were proving that Fermi was in fact splitting the uranium atom into two much lighter atoms by his neutron bombardment: this was atomic FISSION. Fermi was quick to realize the implication of this new interpretation. Each time the atom split, more neutrons were released. Perhaps fission could continue in a self-supporting chain, thereby releasing energy all the time from inside the atomic nucleus.

A group of Fermi's colleagues persuaded Albert EINSTEIN to write to President Roosevelt, drawing his attention to the fact that 'extremely powerful bombs of a new type' might be made in this way—and hinted that the Germans might already be engaged in their development.

The result was an immediate influx of money to develop nuclear power. Fermi's team began serious work on a nuclear reactor, using large graphite blocks to slow the neutrons because it was found that water absorbed too many neutrons.

The reactor effort progressed under great secrecy. There were problems of obtaining sufficiently pure graphite and uranium. A series of experimental piles—an apt description of the reactor's brick-like construction—were built before success was finally achieved.

Fermi's earlier work had shown that cadmium was particularly good at absorbing slow neutrons. Therefore cadmium rods were built into the pile to control the chain reaction rate. It was as these were withdrawn on 2 December 1942 that the first controlled CHAIN REACTION began—and Fermi had ushered in the atomic age.

After this first success of what was called the Manhattan Project, Fermi went to Los Alamos, New Mexico, to work on the atomic bomb. After World War 2 he joined the faculty at the University of Chicago, where the Institute for Nuclear Studies was eventually named after him. He wrote textbooks on various aspects of physics and was regarded as a gifted teacher as well as a research scientist. He collected a great many distinctions besides the Nobel prize, and was at the peak of his powers when he died, barely 53 years old.

FERROMAGNETISM (see magnetic materials)

Below: Enrico Fermi shown operating a 100 million volt particle accelerator at the University of Chicago in May 1950.

FERTILIZER

Fertilizers are applied to the soil, or sometimes directly to the plant, to supply nutrients essential for plant growth. The fertilizer may replace these substances as they are used up by the plant, or may be applied to mineral deficient soils to make them more productive. Many nutrient chemical elements such as copper, boron, manganese, zinc and silicon are only required in minute quantities. Other elements are much more important, and are needed by the plant in large quantities. These major nutrients are nitrogen, phosphorus, potassium, magnesium, calcium, iron, and sulphur, all of which are readily removed from the soil by plants, particularly under conditions of intensive cultivation. Most fertilizers are intended to replace these important nutrient elements.

Manures Fertilizers are basically artificial mixtures of synthetic or naturally occurring substances. Manures, however, are composed of organic material, such as animal dung or various kinds of plant material. They often have the additional property of improving the texture of the soil, and giving it better water-retaining properties. Seaweed was formerly used for this purpose, and is still often used to help break down heavy clay soils.

Manures contain a high proportion of nitrogen, which is essential for plant growth. Atmospheric nitrogen is normally 'fixed' and made available to the plant by bacteria present either in the soil, or sometimes in bacteria living in nodules on the plant roots. The plant can only use the nitrogen after it has been incorporated into a chemical compound. Most manures are produced by *composting*, which is a process designed to encourage bacterial breakdown of dung or plant material into a form readily used by the plant, and it is this process which results in the high nitrogen content of the manure.

Modern livestock farming techniques produce huge quantities of waste material, mostly as semi-liquid cattle dung and poultry droppings, and the problem of disposal of this material without polluting the environment has led to renewed interest

After manufacture, granulated compound fertilizer, consisting of nitrogen, phosphate and potash, is delivered by conveyer to this huge storage silo, where the excavator digs it out for bagging or bulk loads.

BASF

PBI

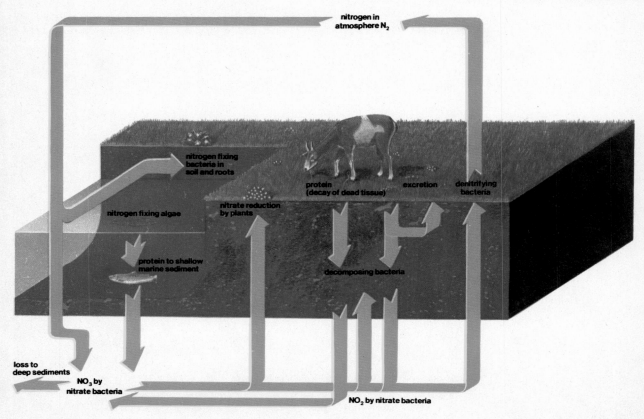

Top: carrots on the left were fed with a liquid fertilizer containing nitrogen, phosphoric acid, potash, trace elements (including magnesium, iron, manganese, molybdenum, boron, zinc, copper and cobalt) and growth stimulants. Those on the right were untreated.

Below: the nitrogen cycle. Atmospheric nitrogen is taken into the soil by nitrogen fixing bacteria and algae. Plants use the nitrogen compounds in protein production. Animals eat the plants and the excreted remains are broken down by bacteria once again.

in large scale manure production. Waste from intensive livestock operations is stored in artificial ponds or lagoons, and the solid matter allowed to settle out while bacterial breakdown takes place. This nitrogen-rich solid material can then be used as agricultural manure. The sludge remaining after purification of sewage is also widely used as a manure, and is particularly in demand for horticultural purposes. A wide range of plant and animal waste-products can be recycled in this way. Sometimes crops are grown especially to be ploughed back into the soil as a manure.

Manures contain variable amounts of nitrogen, and may be deficient in other major nutrient elements. As a good supply of nitrogen is important to stimulate the growth of leaves, manures have been largely replaced by fertilizers in the agricultural industry, allowing the quantities of nitrogen and the other elements to be carefully controlled.

Fertilizers Ammonium sulphate, $(NH_4)_2SO_4$, and ammonium nitrate, NH_4NO_3, are typical nitrogenous fertilizers. They can be prepared in large quantities quite cheaply, and do not present problems in storage or application to crops, in contrast to manures. Ammonium nitrate is produced by reacting ammonia gas with nitric acid. Ammonium sulphate can be made by reacting ammonia gas with sulphuric acid or by the reaction of calcium sulphate and a solution of ammonium carbonate.

Phosphorus is another very important element, often not present in the soil in sufficient quantities. It can be supplied in the form of bone meal, which is the powder remaining after crushing and grinding bones when other valuable chemicals have been extracted. Nowadays phosphorus is usually applied in the form of superphosphate or triple superphosphate.

DIAGRAM VISUAL INFORMATION LTD

nitrogen in atmosphere N$_2$

nitrogen fixing bacteria in soil and roots

nitrogen fixing algae

nitrate reduction by plants

protein (decay of dead tissue)

excretion

denitrifying bacteria

protein to shallow marine sediment

decomposing bacteria

loss to deep sediments

NO$_3$ by nitrate bacteria

NO$_2$ by nitrate bacteria

Superphosphate is produced by treating naturally occurring rock phosphates with sulphuric acid, and contains about 20% phosphorus. Triple superphosphate is manufactured by treating rock phosphate with phosphoric acid, and contains nearly 50% phosphorus. Basic slag, a by-product of STEEL MANUFACTURE, is another good source of phosphorus. Phosphorus is particularly important to establish good root growth in the plant, and to encourage early maturity and ripening.

Potassium is necessary to encourage good growth, and helps produce resistance to disease. It is usually obtained from natural potassium sulphate, K_2SO_4, or potassium chloride, KCl.

Availability to the plant
Fertilizers and manures are used by plants at different rates. Manure cannot be used by the plant until it is broken down into soluble chemicals which can be absorbed by the roots. Some liquid fertilizers, such as those used for horticultural purposes, contain only soluble nutrients, and these are absorbed and used very rapidly. Foliar or leaf feeds are applied to the leaves rather than the soil, and are absorbed through the *stomata*, the tiny holes through which the plant breathes: 90% of a foliar feed is absorbed and used by the plant, as against only 10% when fertilizer is applied to the soil. Foliar feeds may also incorporate substances such as growth stimulants or trace elements which are not readily absorbed from the soil. Though relatively expensive, they are particularly useful in horticulture.

It is often desirable to use fertilizers in a slow-acting form, so that frequent re-application can be avoided. Like manure, most organic fertilizers containing nitrogen break down slowly in the soil, and are available to the plant over a long period. Hoof and horn meal is a naturally occurring, slow-acting nitrogenous fertilizer, and urea, $CO(NH_2)_2$, is a synthetic

Top: an example of the use of the compound fertilizer seen in the picture on page 959. Its marked effect on barley growth, left, compared with the control plants on the right can be clearly seen.

Below: production of ammonium nitrate. Nitric acid is combined with a conditioning solution and then neutralized with ammonia in a safe, two stage boiling process. The 89% ammonium nitrate solution is then evaporated and sprayed into a prilling and cooling tower. The solidified fertilizer is now ready for packing and storage.

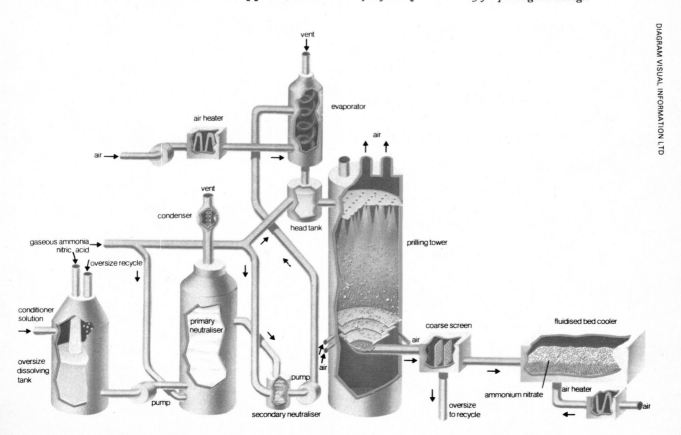

slow-acting source of nitrogen. It is often used today in the form of urea condensates, that is, combined with formaldehyde, crotonaldehyde and isobutyraldehyde. These are, in fact, unstable resins (plastics) that break down in the soil, releasing urea.

Application to the soil or plant
Fertilizers are often compounded into granules or pellets, allowing a balanced mixture of essential nutrients to be supplied. Granules and pellets can be made which will break down at a predetermined rate to give a continuous supply of nutrients to the growing plants. Some crops need one or other of the major nutrients at different points in their growing cycles, so applications of fertilizers must be carefully timed to provide the correct nutrient balance when it is most needed.

Fertilizers and manures can be applied to the soil or plant by a wide variety of means, ranging from simple hand application to machine spreading. Manures are often scattered on the soil and then ploughed in. Sometimes liquefied waste from intensive livestock units is sprayed or pumped on to the pasture as a source of nitrogen. It has been suggested that this practice may spread livestock disease, and might also cause human infection with the organisms causing some types of food poisoning.

Most mineral or synthetic fertilizers are applied by top-dressing, or mechanical spreading on the soil. This is sometimes carried out on a very large scale, such as the application of superphosphate over huge areas of inaccessible land in New Zealand by means of crop spraying aircraft. This resulted in a changed ecology throughout the area, making it suitable for sheep farming. For horticultural purposes, fertilizers are usually applied as a quick acting spray.

FIBREBOARD (see manufactured board)

FIBRE, natural
Fibres are the raw material from which textiles are made for clothing, household, floor covering and industrial uses. For convenience fibres are generally classified as being either natural or manmade, that is, formed by chemical processes, usually involving extrusion of the fibre.

In 1971 the 'free' world production of natural fibres was estimated at 17,832,000 tons, while manmade fibres was 8,415,000 tons. Natural fibre production, however, was stable or increased only slightly in the years 1950–1971, while manmade production expanded steadily, with a fourfold increase in the period. While manmade fibres have relied on petrochemical expansion which is currently in question, natural fibre production expansion is difficult owing to high production costs and competition for land utilization.

The use of natural fibres goes back to the Stone Age when flax and hemp were exploited. Eventually wool, silk and cotton fibres were discovered and were known to have been in use for several thousand years BC. In mediaeval times wool processing was a major occupation, but industrial processing, involving mainly wool and cotton, dates from about 1750.

In modern times, all three natural kingdoms, animal, vegetable and mineral, supply textile fibres.

Animal fibres
The hair of many mammals is potentially useful for textiles, but the principal fibre is sheep's wool. A wide range of breeds of sheep are used to provide wool differing in fineness from lamb's wool ('baby' wool), Merino (fine and soft), crossbred (medium wool for mixing and domestic fabrics) to upland and mountain types (coarse and wiry for carpets).

Below: flax being harvested in Belgium. Flax was one of the first fibres cultivated by man. It is used to make linen and linseed oil.

Wool, clipped or sheared from sheep, or *slain wool* liberated chemically from the skins of dead sheep, is not of constant quality from the same animal, and distinction is made between fine, coarse, outercoat and kemp hairs, which are thick white fibres. Wool *sorting*, usually at the country of origin, achieves separation according to intended use.

Each wool fibre consists of the protein *keratin*, and is built up of spindle-shaped cells. The main cell material or *cortex* is covered by a layer of thin overlapping scales (cuticle), which is visible under a microscope and gives wool its characteristic ability to FELT. Pigment streaks in coloured wools are distributed in the cortex. Wool often has a *crimp wave* which gives it springiness and warmth in products.

The principal producing areas are Australia, New Zealand, South Africa and South America, although most countries with appreciable pasture produce wool.

Other animal fibres in use include goat hairs—chiefly mohair from the Angora goat, cashmere from the cashmere goat, and common goat—camel, llama, rabbit, horse, and cow.

Silk is of animal origin, and is the extrudate or spun thread of the silkworm *Bombyx mori*. Its natural function is to provide a cocoon around the worm, in which metamorphosis into a silk-moth will take place.

Cultivated silk is produced under factory conditions, mulberry leaves being provided for the worms which, on hatching out of eggs, grow to several centimetres in length and contain twin sacs of *fibroin* or liquid silk protein. When it is ready to spin its cocoon, the worm attaches itself to a twig and extrudes the whole of its fibroin by muscular action through a small hole or spinneret, forming a cocoon of endless thread, several kilometres long. Since the emerging moth would break open the cocoon and spoil the thread continuity, the cocoons are stifled with heat, steam or other gas. Next the cocoons are floated on water and *reeled*, several filaments being combined to form a yarn which is fine and lustrous. Japan and China are the main producing countries.

Wild silk, especially *tussah* and *anaphé*, is obtained from cocoons found in the open in Far Eastern countries. These cocoons are usually communal, and also broken, and cannot be reeled. The fibre is recovered by mechanical action and forms cut or staple fibre which is made into yarn by twisting. A typical fabric made from this source is *shantung*.

Vegetable fibres These fibres are numerous and can be divided into seed hairs, bast (inner bark), leaf and fruit fibres.

COTTON is a seed hair, the plant producing numerous large seed pods from each of which radiate thousands of cotton fibres. These fibre clusters, or *bolls*, together with the seeds, are picked mechanically and processed in a COTTON GIN to separate the seeds from the hairs, which are subsequently spun into yarn.

The cotton fibre is a single cell, originally growing as a tube with a cell wall of nearly pure cellulose. When the boll 'bursts' or opens, the fibres dry out and, when viewed under a microscope, resemble twisted flattened tubes. Cotton will spin into very fine yarns and is known for comfort and coolness. *Mercerization* is the treatment of cotton yarn or fabric with a concentrated sodium hydroxide solution, producing enhanced lustre and smoothness.

Kapok is a seed hair, from a tree, and is used only for stuffing and (formerly) as a flotation material in lifejackets.

Bast fibres, or soft fibres, are recovered from the stems (phloem and cortex) of various dicotyledonous plants such as flax, jute, hemp, kenaf, surn and ramie (or China grass). Flax

Below: sisal is Kenya's third largest export. It is a coarse fibre that is used to make twine and rough fabrics.

COLORIFIC

(synonymous with linen) is used for clothing, but the others are mainly used for industrial textiles and floorcoverings. Jute is the most widely used member of this group.

The plant stems need *retting*, which is controlled rotting by soaking in water and allowing bacteria to attack the stems. The fibres are then separated mechanically by *scutching* (beating). The fibres are bundles of many overlapping cellulosic cells and are much thicker, stiffer and longer than cotton. The cells adhere by means of *lignin* cement.

Jute is grown in Bangladesh and India. Flax, formerly important in Northern Ireland, grows in the USSR, Poland, and Belgium.

Leaf fibres, or hard fibres, are similarly constructed but are obtained from the leaf, stem or stalks of monocotyledonous plants. Mechanical separation only is necessary. Sisal and abaca (or Manila) are the main commercial examples. The main sources of sisal are Tanzania, Mexico and the Philippines, the latter being the source of Manila, which is very rot resistant.

Fruit fibres are mainly represented by coir or coconut fibre, which is obtained from between the outer husk and shell of the coconut. The fibre is reddish brown, stiff and wiry, and is used for matting. Countries producing coir include India and Sri Lanka.

Mineral fibre   The term ASBESTOS covers the fibrous mineral silicates, mined in Canada and South Africa. The rock form is often greenish in colour, but after crushing the whitish soft fibres are obtained. These fibres are brittle and weak, but very resistant chemically and fireproof. Asbestos is therefore mainly used for insulation and protective clothing.

Top: *early cleaning of raw material in cotton processing.*

Above: *a silk factory. The cocoons are smothered to kill the worm inside; then the silk must be unwound and reeled. Cocoons of wild silk are broken and cannot be wound; they are twisted to make yarn.*

Right: *wool. The use of animal and vegetable fibres is among the oldest accomplishments of mankind; their production and distribution has always been of great importance to the world's economy.*

FIBRE, synthetic

Manmade or synthetic fibres occupy a very important position in the world textile industry today, and they are produced in vast quantities by carefully controlled techniques. As with many other products, the story of manmade fibres began with attempts to manufacture an alternative to a natural product—in this case silk. Manmade fibres, however, could develop only as fast as the development of man's understanding of the chemistry of fibres.

The first idea of manufacturing fibres was recorded as early as 1664, but it was some two hundred years later before serious attempts were made to implement the idea. Then, in 1888, Sir Joseph Swan patented a process for making nitrocellulose filaments, subsequently converted to cellulose, for making not textiles but filaments for electric lamps. Within the next ten years Chardonnet had exhibited artificial silk fabrics at the Paris Exhibition of 1889, and the *cuprammonium* and *viscose* processes for making artificial silk from cellulose had been discovered. These fibres were later named *rayons*. The manmade fibre industry had begun, and the production of viscose and cuprammonium rayons increased steadily. In the early 1920s another manmade fibre—*cellulose acetate*—was introduced.

The next twenty years were a period of great activity in the study of polymer chemistry and this led to the possibility of producing completely synthetic fibres. *Nylon* was discovered by W H Carothers in America in 1934—in time to have an important use in World War 2 for making parachutes. *Polyester* fibres were discovered in England in 1941, and were launched commercially in the 1950s, as were several *acrylic* and *triacetate*

fibres. At the same time fibres were being made from PROTEINS derived from skimmed milk, ground nuts, maize or soya beans, but these were never really successful in the face of competition from other new fibres.

Today, there are 23 generic types of fibres which are recognized in official lists, and this number is still increasing, but the consumer will usually only encounter some of these. For example, the important fibre groups for clothing, furnishings and household textiles are acetate, acrylic, nylon (*polyamide*), polyester, rayon (viscose and *modal*) and triacetate. Other groups, such as *chlorofibres*, *elastofibres*, GLASS FIBRE, metallic yarns, *modacrylic*, polyethylene and *polypropylene*, are produced in smaller quantities but have important uses in the domestic market.

The reason there are so many types of fibre is that each group possesses a different combination of physical characteristics, which determine their usefulness in the textile industry. A fibre can survive commercially only if it can contribute to the expanding performance and design requirements of the textile industry.

Fibres, both natural and manmade, are composed of long chain polymers, with the molecules aligned roughly along the fibre length. Properties that a synthetic fibre polymer must have include good tensile strength and a high melting point, so that it will not disintegrate during ironing.

The normal manufacturing processes for synthetic fibres have certain features in common. The polymer is converted to liquid form by dissolving it in a solvent or by melting it, and the liquid is extruded through a spinneret (jet). The extruded

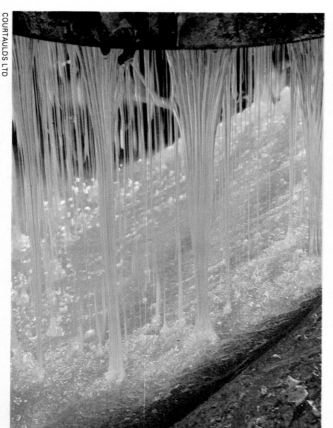

Above: the dry spinning of an acetate yarn by extrusion through a jet assembly into a heated airstream which evaporates the solvent, allowing the fibres to form.

Left: the syrupy orange 'viscose', which is chemically ripened and then spun in a bath of chemicals to solidify the fibres into rayon. Most rayons are now produced by the viscose process, which was discovered in 1892, and have a wide range of uses including clothing, furnishing textiles, carpets, industrial textiles, and tyre cords.

filaments are solidified by precipitation or evaporation of a solvent, or simply by cooling. The filaments are then drawn (stretched) to cause the polymer molecules to lie more parallel to the fibre length, and this increases the strength of the fibres. Manmade fibres are made in the form of continuous filament yarn or as staple fibre (short lengths) for the production of spun yarns.

Rayons The word 'rayon' has for years been used as a collective name for all manmade cellulose fibres, but it is becoming more common to divide the rayon into two groups—viscose rayon (the standard rayon) and modal, modified from the standard rayon.

The terms viscose and cupro are taken from the names of manufacturing processes. The cuprammonium process, in which the cellulose is dissolved in cuprammonium hydroxide, is no longer used in Britain, but is still used in some countries for producing special types of yarn. The viscose process, discovered in England in 1892, is the basis of the vast majority of rayon and modified rayon production today. The basic viscose process consists of several clearly defined stages.

The process starts by steeping wood pulp in a caustic soda solution, which converts the pulp into soda cellulose and at the same time extracts certain impurities from the wood pulp. The excess alkali is squeezed out and the swollen pulp is shredded into fine crumbs. After ageing, the soda cellulose

Below: Celon production. Caprolactam, titania and water, the raw materials for Celon, are heated to 260° for about 20 hours until polymerized and then extruded into the quench bath for cooling and solidification. The polymer cable is cut into chips, washed and then dried in a vacuum tumble drier.

crumbs are treated with carbon disulphide to form the bright orange cellulose xanthate. This is dissolved in dilute caustic soda to give an orange coloured syrup known as *viscose*. After 'ripening' to the right chemical state, the viscose is spun into a bath containing dilute sulphuric acid, sodium sulphate and zinc sulphate which causes the fibre to solidify at a rate which permits the yarn to be stretched.

The basic process has been modified in a number of ways to produce a range of fibres with quite different properties: high tenacity viscose such as Tenasco and Tyrex for use in tyre cords and other industrial purposes; crimped viscose for use in carpets, upholstery and clothing; high wet modulus (modal) for clothing and domestic textiles; and flame resistant fibres. All rayons are absorbent and therefore give comfort in use. They are used extensively in all sections of the textile industry, sometimes alone, but often blended with other fibres.

Acetate and triacetate Acetate and triacetate are the generic names for fibres made from cellulose acetate and cellulose triacetate respectively. Chemically, triacetate is a fully acetylated cellulose obtained by reacting cellulose from wood pulp with acetic acid in the presence of a CATALYST, for example sulphuric acid.

Cellulose acetate is formed by diluting this solution of triacetate with water and allowing it to stand. Hydrolysis (chemical decomposition by the action of water) takes place slowly, some of the acetyl groups being replaced by the original hydroxyl groups of cellulose. This process is stopped by diluting with an excess of water when approximately one in six of the acetyl groups have been removed. The resulting product is known as cellulose acetate or simply acetate.

Fibres are produced by dissolving the polymer in an organic

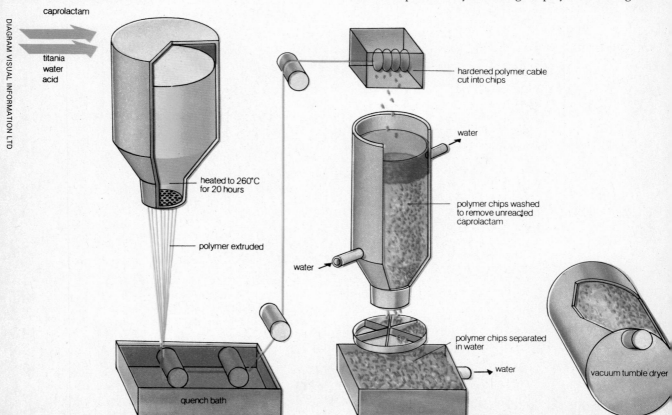

caprolactam

titania
water
acid

heated to 260°C for 20 hours

polymer extruded

quench bath

water

water

hardened polymer cable cut into chips

water

polymer chips washed to remove unreacted caprolactam

polymer chips separated in water

water

vacuum tumble dryer

solvent, acetone for cellulose acetate, and methylene chloride for cellulose triacetate. The viscous solution is extruded not through a spinneret, as with rayon, but simply into a stream of hot air which causes the solvent to evaporate and the fibres to be formed. This is known as a dry spinning process as opposed to the wet spinning method used in the viscose process.

Cellulose triacetate fibres were produced as long ago as 1914, but the only known solvent at that time was chloroform—both expensive and dangerous. Also the fibre could not be dyed with the dyes then available, and as a result the commercial introduction of this fibre was delayed for 40 years.

Cellulose acetate dissolved in acetone was used extensively in World War 1 for coating aeroplane wings and this left, at the end of the war, a capacity for producing cellulose acetate but no market for it. Cellulose acetate was easier to spin into fibres than the triacetate but was also very difficult to dye. Fortunately, in 1923 a completely new class of dye was discovered which would dye cellulose acetate fibres. This discovery was important not only for acetate in the 1920s but also in later years for the nylons, polyesters, acrylics and triacetates. Today acetate, sold under trade marks such as Dicel (UK) and Estron (USA), is noted for its silk-like appearance and is used extensively in furnishings, and clothing.

Triacetate, sold as Tricel (UK) and Arnel (USA), is nearer to the fully synthetic fibres in that it can be durably pleated or set and has easy care, quick drying properties. Triacetate is used in dresses, knitwear, underwear, linings—and in household textiles such as bedspreads and bath mats.

Nylon (polyamide)
Nylon and polyamide are recognized alternative generic names for this group of fibres, nylon being used mainly in the UK and North America and poly-amide in continental Europe. There are a number of nylons but they are all characterized by the presence of amide (—CO—NH—) linkages in the polymer chain. They are produced by the polymerization of an AMINO ACID or the corresponding *lactam* (a cyclic acid formed from amino acids) or by the copolymerization of a diamine with a diacid. The most common nylons are nylon 6 and nylon 66. Nylon 6 is produced by polymerizing caprolactam, and nylon 66 by copolymerizing hexamethylene diamine and adipic acid to form polyhexamethylene adipamide. Hexamethylene diamine, adipic acid and caprolactam are all produced by chemical reaction from oil refining products such as benzene or cyclohexane.

The numbers 6 and 66 refer to the number of carbon atoms in the chemical compound or compounds which are polymerized. A single number indicates a self-polymerized compound, while a double number denotes a combination of two compounds for the basic polymer link.

Nylon fibres are *melt spun*, that is, the polymer 'chips' are melted in an inert atmosphere to prevent degradation, and the molten liquid is extruded through a spinneret. The filaments formed solidify by cooling. After spinning, the filaments are cold drawn to several times their original length and this greatly increases the strength and general serviceability.

From the outset nylon was an astounding fibre. It was strong and resilient and hence hard wearing. It was a thermoplastic

Below : production and processing of Celon. Polymer chips are melted and extruded through a series of fine holes. The filaments are cooled, then lubricated, and finally wound onto a package called a cheese. During processing the yarn is fed through a drawtwisting machine which orientates and strengthens the filaments.

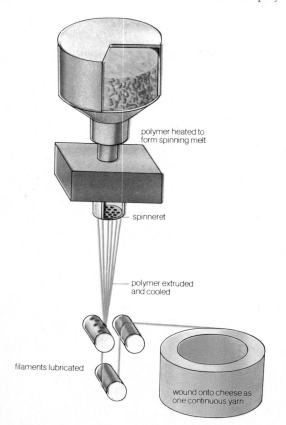

polymer heated to form spinning melt

spinneret

polymer extruded and cooled

filaments lubricated

wound onto cheese as one continuous yarn

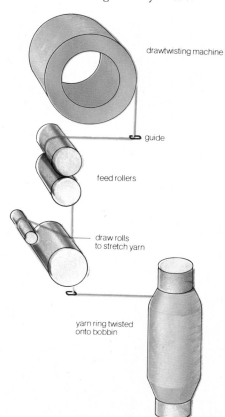

drawtwisting machine

guide

feed rollers

draw rolls to stretch yarn

yarn ring twisted onto bobbin

DIAGRAM VISUAL INFORMATION LTD

fibre and could be heat set to give easy-care fabrics. Moreover the ability to be heat set enabled the development of crimped and stretch yarns widely used today in hosiery. Nylon took over the majority of the women's stockings market and, because of its high strength, finer gauge stockings became possible. Nylon today is used in almost every textile application, and has many industrial uses. It is manufactured in many countries under names such as Bri-nylon, Celon and Enkalon (UK) and Antron (USA). Nylon fibres with trilobal ('cloverleaf') cross-sections have been made to give the diffuse glitter seen in certain fabrics. Recently, antistatic nylons have also been introduced.

Polyesters
Polyester is the generic name for fibres made of polyethylene terephthalate—obtained from reacting ethylene glycol (see ALCOHOL) with terephthalic acid.

As with nylon, the raw materials are oil refining products, in this case paraxylene and ethylene which are converted into terephthalic acid and ethylene glycol respectively. The fibres are produced by melt spinning and are drawn out subsequently to increase their strength.

Polyester fibres are produced in large quantities throughout the world and well known brand names such as Terylene, Crimplene, Lirelle, Terlenka, Trevira (UK) and Dacron and Fortrel (USA). Polyester fabrics have set new standards of high performance and easy care in suitings and dresses, shirts and household textiles. Suitings and trouserings have been mainly polyester-wool, polyester-cotton and polyester-rayon blends, but recently have included 100% polyester knitted fabrics. Large quantities of knitted textured polyester and woven polyester-cotton are used in dresses. Polyester fibres are also used extensively in blends with rayon, acrylics, triacetate and nylons. Polyester, like nylon, has a wide range of industrial uses.

Acrylics
Acrylic fibres are made from polyacrylonitrile obtained by polymerizing acrylonitrile. This chemical can be produced in a number of ways, one of which is to react propylene, another oil refining product, with ammonia.

The fibres are often wet spun, that is extruded into an aqueous coagulating bath, but some are dry spun.

Acrylics are renowned for their softness combined with high performance and easy care properties. Ingenious methods have been developed for producing high bulk yarns to enhance the softness and warmth. The growth of this group of fibres has been very rapid and their brand names like Acrilan, Orlon, Courtelle and Dralon are well known. They are widely used in knitwear and knitted fabrics generally, pile fabrics and imitation furs, dresses, furnishings and carpets. Frequently acrylics are used on their own but increasingly they are being used in conjunction with nylon, polyester, wool or viscoses.

Modacrylics are fibres made from copolymers of acrylonitrile with vinyl or vinylidene chloride or both. They are very similar to acrylics in textile properties, but additionally can be flame resistant and are finding increasing uses where flame resistance is required.

Other groups of fibres
Although the remaining fibre groups are produced in smaller quantities, they nevertheless have important uses in the textile industry. The elastofibres (also referred to as elastomerics or spandex) have the generic name *elastane* and *elastodiene* in the International Standard list. They extend and recover like rubber, and are being widely used as power nets for support garments and swimwear under trade marks such as Spanzelle and Lycra.

Glass fibre is used in curtains but is mainly an industrial fibre for laminating with resins. Chlorofibres, made essentially from vinyl or vinylidene chloride, provide flameproof fabrics for furnishings and certain clothing. Metallic yarns such as Lurex are usually coated aluminium foil, to give a glitter effect.

Polyethylene yarns are well known as the material used for deck chairs and orange fishing nets. Polypropylene is used in cordage and carpet backing, and as slit film yarn in sacks and packaging materials.

There are other groups which will seldom be encountered because they are purely for industrial purposes or are produced locally in other parts of the world. One of the most recent of these is CARBON FIBRE which is used for making high performance laminates with resins.

Above: synthetic fibres can be spun into yarns and knitted or woven into cloth. This picture, taken through a microscope, shows a piece of knitted acrylic fibre.

Left: synthetic fibre being deposited into drums to dry at a factory in Spartanburg, South Carolina, USA.